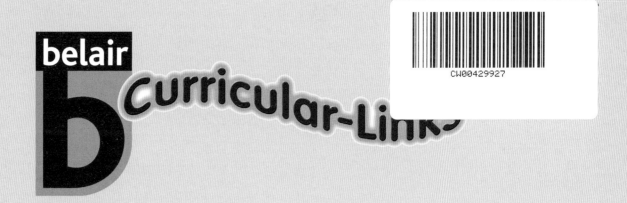

belair
Curricular-Links

Science 3

fabulous   food

Broccoli

Cauliflower

Chicken

Sweetcorn

Carrots

Potato   Peas

Elaine Chantler

Acknowledgements

I would like to offer my grateful thanks to the headteacher, Anne Siggins, and the staff and pupils of Priory Fields Primary School, Dover, in particular to Helen Seeley, Jenni Mulraney, Marie-Anne Long, Lynne Taylor, Bubbles Bence, Julie Cook, Ali Poole and Debbie Bailey for their much appreciated assistance with creating displays for this book.

My thanks also go to Chris Martin, Zoë Parish and Steve Forest.

I would like to dedicate this book to my wonderful mum Margaret.

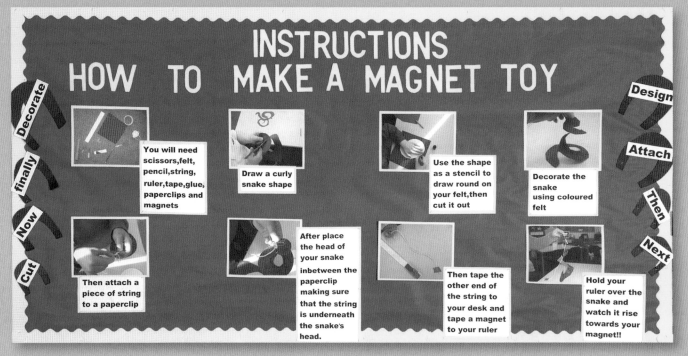

From Magnets and Springs on page 72

Commissioning Editor: Zoë Parish   Editor: Kim Richardson   Cover Design: Sophie Pelham
Page Layout: Martin Cross   Photography: Steve Forest   Illustrations: Martin Pierce

First Published in 2008 by Belair Publications.

Every effort has been made to trace the copyright holders of material used in this publication. If any copyright holder has been overlooked, we should be pleased to make the necessary arrangements.

British Library Cataloguing in the Publication Data. A catalogue record for this publication is available from the British Library.

ISBN 978-1-84191-463-3

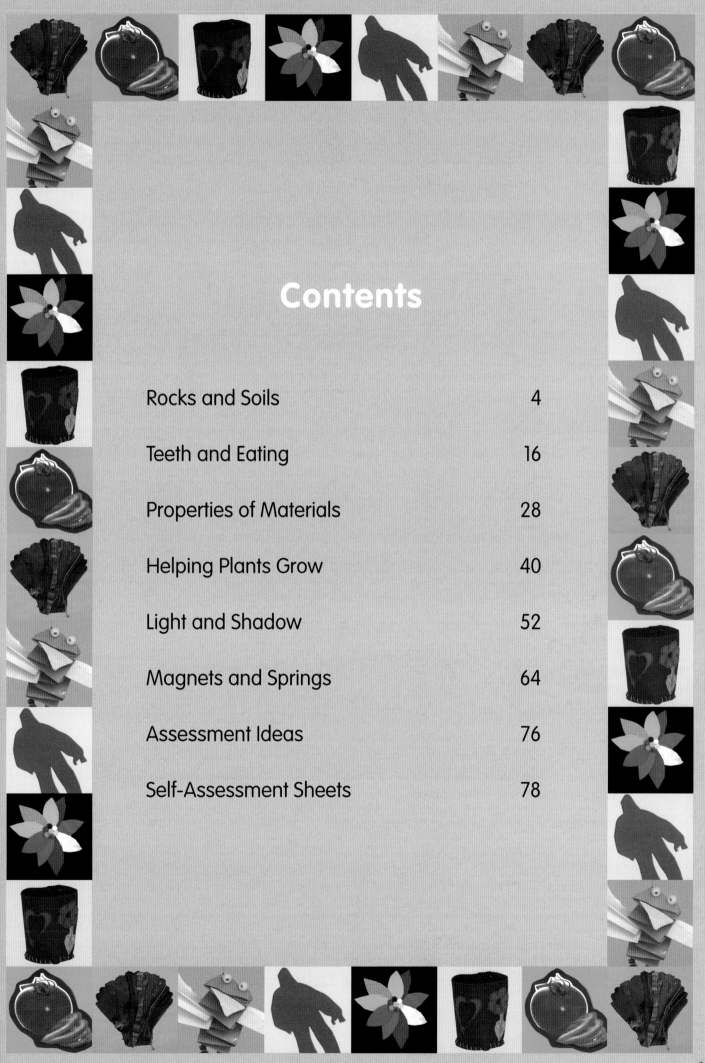

Contents

Rocks and Soils   4

Teeth and Eating   16

Properties of Materials   28

Helping Plants Grow   40

Light and Shadow   52

Magnets and Springs   64

Assessment Ideas   76

Self-Assessment Sheets   78

Rocks and Soils

These grids demonstrate the learning objectives covered in the activities within the theme. The curriculum references indicate the relevant programme of study (PoS) for a subject area unless otherwise stated.

	Learning Objectives	Curriculum References
Science (Page 6)		
Scientific Enquiry	Consider current knowledge of rocks and soils and pose questions to be explored and answered.	Sc1/2a,b
	Make predictions about the properties of rock. Plan and conduct investigations from initial lines of enquiry.	Sc1/1b;2c
	Observe rocks and soils and record from first hand experience. Analyse and discuss results, drawing conclusions.	Sc1/2f,i,j
Materials and their Properties (QCA Science Unit 3D)	Handle, discuss and sort rocks and soils according to a range of criteria.	Sc3/1d
	Observe and describe changes that happen when rocks and soils are combined with water or are rubbed against other materials.	Sc3/2a
	Recognise that some, but not all materials dissolve in water.	Sc3/3b
Literacy (Page 8)		
Listening and Responding	Present information to others about rocks and soils.	En1/1b,c
	Ask a farmer or gardener questions, identifying key points.	En1/2a-d;3a
Creating and Shaping Texts	Write text for a PowerPoint® presentation about rocks and soils.	En3/1a; ICT PoS 2a;3a
	Write imaginative text about animals that live in the soil.	En3/1b,c
	Plan and compose calligrams about features of rocks and soils.	En3/1a;2a,b,e
Understanding and Interpreting Texts	Read information texts about rocks and soils and identify the key points.	En2/3a,c
Mathematics (Page 10)		
Knowing and using Number Facts	Use fossils and shells to explore multiples and related division facts.	Ma2/2b;3a
Using and Applying Mathematics	Use appropriate methods of calculation to solve two-step number problems about animals that live underground.	Ma2/1b;3a
Measuring	Recognise and use appropriate units of measurement during an investigation about the effect of liquids on rocks and soils.	Ma3/4a
	Read numbers on a scale.	Ma3/4b
Understanding Shape	Can transform objects by rotation.	Ma3/3b
Handling Data	Present findings about rocks and soils in a suitable manner.	Ma4/1f;2c; ICT PoS 1b
	Interpret charts and tables and construct own diagrams.	Ma4/2b,c

Rocks and Soils

Learning Objectives	Curriculum References
Geography (Page 12)	
Describe the sense of place using appropriate geographical terminology.	PoS 3a-c, QCA Unit 6
Identify the area to be investigated on an aerial photograph or by using maps at varying scales.	PoS 2c,d
Carry out fieldwork using skills and techniques such as sketching, note-taking, photography and map-making.	PoS 2b,e
Identify physical or human processes, such as erosion, that may be acting on the locality, causing change.	PoS 4b
PSHCE (Page 12)	
Identify and recognise the potential risks to one's own safety when choosing places to play.	PoS 3e
Make suggestions as to how to behave in a safe, sensible way around our coastline.	PoS 3e
Recognise when someone is behaving in a risky way.	PoS 3f
Design & Technology (Page 14)	
Discuss steps to be followed to create a shell mobile.	PoS 1a-d
Select and use tools and techniques needed to create shells. Create and assemble these to produce a mobile.	PoS 2a,b,d
PE (Page 14)	
Use music stimuli as a starting point for a dance sequence about fossils.	PoS 6b
Perform the dance, identifying how the music has been successfully interpreted through movement.	PoS 3a
RE (Page 14)	
Compare the views of different cultures and religions about the creation of the Earth with those of a geologist. Conduct a debate, respecting all views.	PoS 1a,d;3a,d
Art (Page 15)	
Draw fossils and shells from first hand observation in a range of media. Use initial sketches as a reference point to inform ongoing projects.	PoS 1a-c
Consider the pattern, shape and textural qualities of fossils and shells and how these can be represented.	PoS 2a;4a
Experiment with the size, shape and combination of images of fossils.	PoS 4a
Use ICT such as digital photography to create a photo-montage of fossils and shells.	PoS 5c; ICT PoS 4b;5b
History (Page 15)	
Place artefacts such as fossils into correct periods of time.	PoS 1a
Use appropriate terminology and dates relating to the history of the Earth.	PoS 1b
Use a variety of sources to gather information about famous geologists.	PoS 4a; ICT PoS 1a; 5b
Music (Page 15)	
Listen attentively to music by Camille Saint-Saëns evoking fossils, identifying elements such as tempo, timbre and dynamics within a piece.	PoS 4a,b
Play tuned instruments with rhythm and control to create own fossil music.	PoS 1b
Use the mood and effect of a recorded piece of music as a starting point for own work.	PoS 2b

Rocks and Soils

Science

Starting Points

- Present the children with a collection of materials, some being rock and some not. Encourage the children to handle and talk about the materials and then to sort them into two groups: rock or not rock. Talk about which items were easy to sort and which were harder. Discuss with the children their reasons for sorting and if necessary correct any errors. Make sure that the children know that soil is formed from rock particles and from organic matter. Use the activity sheet on page 7.

- Explain that pebbles and stones are small pieces of rock. Look at named samples of rock, such as marble, slate, chalk, sandstone and granite, and sort according to observable criteria such as colour or texture. See the display above for ideas.

Enquiry

- Conduct an experiment to assess the hardness of different rock types. Ask the children to rub two identical rock samples together to see what happens. Children should observe any changes in the rock samples that occur and examine any particles of rock that may have been rubbed off the sample. Repeat the test with several different types of rock and then ask the children to rank the rock samples from most able to least able to withstand rubbing. What conclusions can the children draw from their results? Which rock do they think would be most suited to the construction of a coastal sea defence or a house and why?

Extension Activities

- To find out about rocks and soils, visit websites such as that of the Natural History Museum, www.nhm.ac.uk, or www.lymeregismuseum.co.uk/fossils.htm.

- Take a field trip to an area of exposed rock, such as a cliff face. Alternatively, look at photographs of rocks found in different parts of the UK.

- Make a soil solution by placing a quantity of garden soil in a transparent beaker of water. Stir the mixture well and then allow it to settle overnight. Ask the children to observe what has happened to the soil and ask for possible explanations.

Rock ... or not?

Which of these are examples of rock? Which are not? Sort them by drawing each one in the appropriate sorting circle below.

shell | brick | chalk | concrete | pebble | fossil | slate | sand | soil | clay

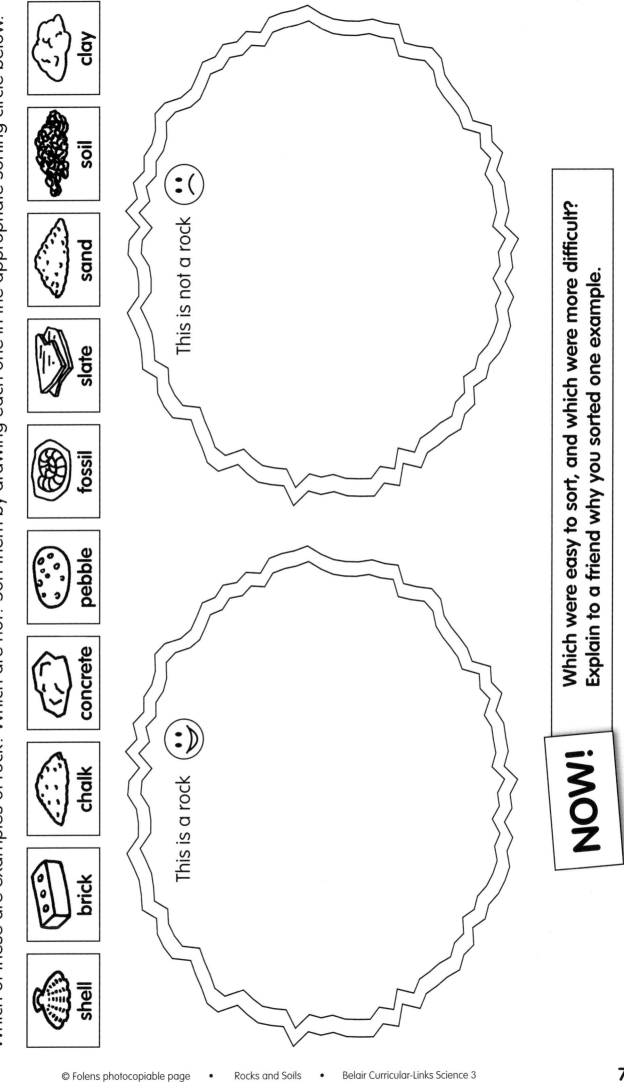

This is a rock ☺

This is not a rock ☹

NOW!

Which were easy to sort, and which were more difficult?
Explain to a friend why you sorted one example.

Literacy

Speaking and Listening

- Ask the children to use images and text to create and present a PowerPoint® presentation about rocks and soils.

- Interview a gardener or local farmer and ask questions about the soil in the local area.

Reading and Writing

- Ask the children to write a non-chronological report of a field trip to a rock face such as a cliff. Rehearse skills of combining text and graphics, using images from the internet or from clip art to enhance passages of text about the trip.

- Write a 'soil menu' for a worm. Make the different types of soil sound appetising to the palate of the worm!

- Ask the children to write detailed descriptions of a fossil such as an ammonite from first-hand observation (see the activity sheet on page 9), or an imaginative account of what the creature might tell us if it came back to life.

- Write calligram poems, describing the different textures of rocks and soils (for ideas see the display above).

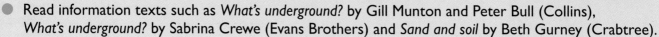

- Read non-fiction books about animals that live in the soil and ask the children to make an information poster about the life under our feet.

- Read information texts such as *What's underground?* by Gill Munton and Peter Bull (Collins), *What's underground?* by Sabrina Crewe (Evans Brothers) and *Sand and soil* by Beth Gurney (Crabtree).

- Read the story *The big bug dug* by Mary Serfozo (published by Scholastic) and talk about the things that the bug comes across as he digs his way underground.

- Ask the children to write a page from the daily diary of a mole.

- Write a 'recipe' to make the perfect soil. Include different rock particles, organic matter and animal life.

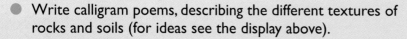

My *fabulous fossil* fact sheet

Draw your fossil here and add labels.

Describe your fossil using the bullet points below. Then write two facts about your fossil.

- _____

- _____

- _____

- _____

- _____

FACT ATTACK!

FASCINATING FACT!

FACT ATTACK!

INCREDIBLE BUT TRUE!

animals in the soil

moles

Mole digs 5 holes on every day of the week.How many holes does he dig in 2 weeks?

ants

An ant lays 70 eggs but only half of them hatch.How many is that?

worms

24 worms live in this hole then 45 come and join them. How many worms altogether?

rabbits

4 rabbits have 100 carrots to share.How many do they have each?

badgers

Badger collected 68 slugs to eat but he gave 19 to his friend. How many slugs did Badger have left?

Maths

Using Number Facts

● Use a shell collection to explore arrays for different numbers, related to multiplication tables.

● Use models of fossils as a resource to aid work on division, including division by grouping. Use the activity sheet on page 11.

Using and Applying

● Use the context of underground animals to pose two-step word problems for the children to solve using appropriate methods (for ideas, see the display above).

rabbits

4 rabbits have 100 carrots to share.How many do they have each?

Measuring

● Review work on capacity when investigating the effects of liquids on rocks and soils. Practise reading numbers on a scale such as that on a measuring jug or cylinder.

Understanding shape

● Use images of pebbles or fossils when working on position and movement. For instance, present the children with an image of a fossil and ask them to predict the position of the image when it is rotated through a series of quarter turns.

Handling Data

● Use researched facts to create a class database on the characteristics of rocks or soils. Pose questions to class members and use the database to answer these questions.

Division by grouping

Help the fossil finders share their fascinating finds!

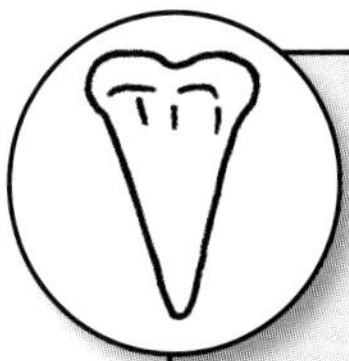

Three archaeologists find 18 fossilised shark teeth. Complete this number line with multiples of 3. Then use it to help you divide 18 by 3, to work out how many teeth each archaeologist can have.

0 [ ] [ ] [ ] [ ] [ ] 18

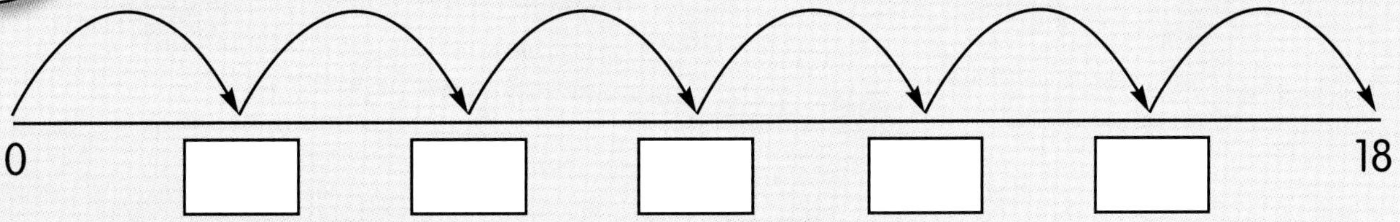

Write how many teeth each archaeologist can have in this box. [ ]

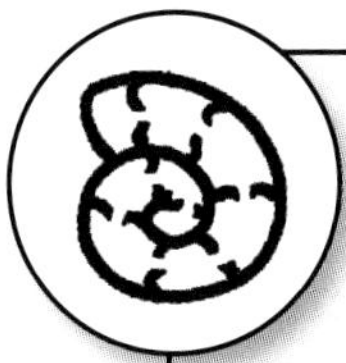

Five scientists find 35 ancient ammonites. Complete this number line with multiples of 5. Then use it to help you divide 35 by 5, to work out how many ammonites each scientist can have.

0 [ ] [ ] [ ] [ ] 25 30 35

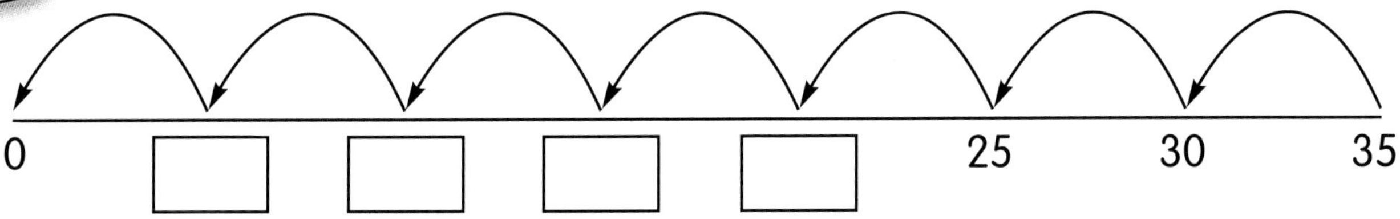

Write how many ammonites each scientist can have in this box. [ ]

Six lucky gardeners find 42 trilobites buried in the soil. Complete this number line with multiples of 6. Then use it to help you divide 42 by 6, to work out how many trilobites each gardener can have.

0 [ ] [ ] [ ] [ ] [ ] 36 42

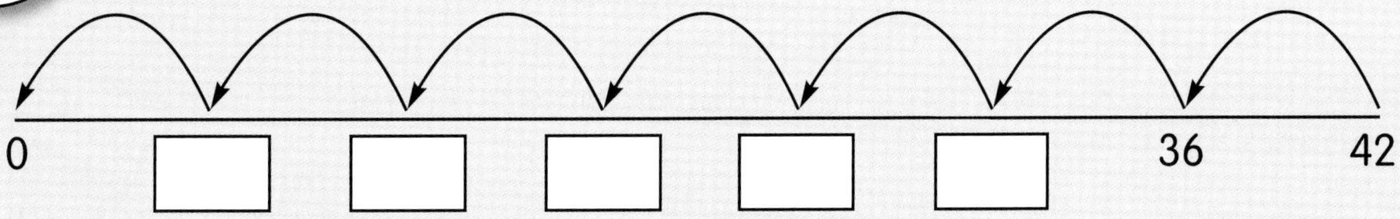

Write how many trilobites each gardener can have in this box. [ ]

Four builders find 36 fossilised fern leaves in slate. Compete this number line with multiples of 4. FIll in the missing numbers that you land on.

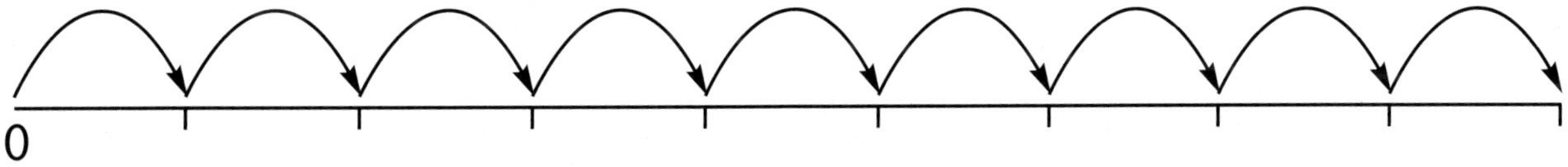

0

Write how many fern leaves each builder can have in this box. [ ]

Geography

- Undertake a field trip to a local area of exposed rock or soil such as at the local beach or at a local archaeological dig. Using photographs or samples as a guide, ask the children to identify the rocks and soils present in the location and suggest reasons for their frequency in certain areas (see display above).

- Through first-hand observation, ask the children to determine any human and physical processes, such as erosion and weathering, which are acting on the rocks or soils in the local area. Discuss the likely outcome of such processes on the landscape in the present day and in the future.

- Make a transect of the locality to record the presence and location of rocks and soils. To do this, lay a long piece of twine/string, or several metre sticks end to end, across the area to be studied, e.g. playing field or wildlife area. Then walk along the line and record what is found immediately below it. Or you could ask the children to sketch or photograph the area, and then identify the human and physical features present. They could then draw a map of the locality.

- Use aerial photographs, maps and charts, including a geological map if possible, to ascertain why a place is like it is and to place the area in a wider geographical context.

- Ask the children to make a field guide or leaflet for visitors to the area, detailing aspects of the local geology and physical features.

- Ask the children to explain what certain geographical terms mean, and test each other. Use the activity sheet on page 13.

PSHCE

- Discuss safe and unsafe places to play. Why do some people indulge in risk-taking behaviour? How can risks be reduced?

- If appropriate to your area, invite the local coastguard in to talk about cliff top safety.

- Look at warning signs and posters that are used around our coastline to keep the public safe.

- Ask the children to design and make a warning triangle sign to alert people to danger, such as the likelihood of rockfall or the danger of crumbling chalk cliffs.

Rocks and Soils

Geographical terms

Explain what is meant by these geographical terms:

EROSION is …

IMPERMEABLE means …

IGNEOUS ROCK means …

STRATA means …

Make a set of fact cards.
Test a friend's knowledge of geographical terms.
Write a glossary of geographical terms.

Design & Technology

- Design a whole-class mobile that could be hung in a communal area of the school, featuring shells or fossils. Ask each child to produce a shell or fossil from sturdy card, to hang on the mobile, decorated with colour co-ordinated strips of materials such as ribbon, lace, sequins and fabric. Make these individual pieces 3-D by adding newspapers as padding between the two outer layers with newspaper. Hang the shells or fossils onto a framework using fishing line or narrow ribbon.

PE

- Listen to a recording of 'Fossils', a short movement from *The carnival of animals* by Camille Saint-Saëns (1835–1921). In small groups, discuss and experiment with sequences of movements with which to interpret the music. Rehearse the movements and then combine to create a pattern or extended sequence, which can be performed to the music.

RE

- Conduct an informed debate about how the Earth was formed. Compare the views of a variety of cultures and religions with the viewpoint of geologists such as Sir Charles Lyell (1797–1875). Stress to the children the importance of respecting other people's points of view, even if they are different from their own.

Art

- Use a variety of media, such as pencils, chalk and pastels, to record observational drawings of fossils and shells.

- Transfer observational drawings of fossils onto chunks of polystyrene using a clay modelling tool, and use the polystyrene block to create mono-prints of fossils using a range of coloured paint and paper.

- Print images of fossils or shells onto fabric and create a whole-class wall hanging.

- Make impressions of fossils and shells in softened plasticine and use these as moulds to produce 3-D work in plaster of Paris.

- Use a digital camera to take close-up images of rock samples, shells and fossils. Using digital images of fossils, experiment with re-sizing and colour to print out and produce a photo-montage (for ideas see display above).

- Create a large, collaborative collage of a fossil such as an ammonite using textured materials.

History

- Investigate the lives of famous geologists such as Sir Charles Lyell (1797–1875) or the Victorian fossil finder Mary Anning (1799–1847).

- Make a visit to a museum that has fossils, such as the Natural History Museum in London, where the children can explore the geology exhibitions in the Earth Galleries.

- Introduce the idea of 'prehistory' and discuss, using appropriate terms, the geological timescale. Use a simplified version of a geological timescale such as that found at www.stratigraphy.org. Attempt to sequence fossils into chronological order.

Music

- Listen again to a recording of 'Fossils' by Camille Saint-Saëns (see PE, page 14) and discuss how the tempo, texture and dynamics have been used to communicate an effect, which evokes fossilized bones.

- Using tuned and untuned instruments, experiment with the effect created by combining sounds. Create a piece of original music, in a style similar to that of 'Fossils'. Use graphic notation to record the work. Perform and record the piece.

Teeth and Eating

These grids demonstrate the learning objectives covered in the activities within the theme. The curriculum references indicate the relevant programme of study (PoS) for a subject area unless otherwise stated.

	Learning Objectives	Curriculum References
Science (Page 18)		
Scientific Enquiry	Plan and conduct an investigation about teeth, predicting likely outcomes.	Sc1/2c
	Make and record observations.	Sc1/2f
	Communicate findings and explain what has happened. Draw conclusions.	Sc1/2h,j,l
Scientific Enquiry Life Processes and Living Things (QCA Science Unit 3A)	Understand nutrition as a basic requirement for life.	Sc2/1a
	Research the different types of teeth and their purpose.	Sc2/2a
	Study the structure of a tooth.	Sc2/2a
	Consider the ways in which humans can take care of their teeth through diet and cleaning.	Sc2/2a
	Ascertain the requirements of a healthy, balanced diet for humans and the role of food in growth and as a source of energy.	Sc2/2b
Literacy (Page 20)		
Listening and Responding	Hold a debate about eating sweets; use a persuasive argument.	En1/2e;3a
	Listen to and re-present a talk about school dinners, summarise main points.	En1/2a,c
Understanding and Interpreting Texts	Read factual texts about teeth and identify key points.	En2/3a,c
Engaging with and Responding to Texts	Read and talk about stories where teeth and eating are a focus.	En2/4g
Creating and Shaping Texts	Write a letter to the tooth fairy.	En3/1a;12
	Write a shopping list and notes.	En3/1a;12
	Write stories about the food journey for a specific audience.	En3/1c
Mathematics (Page 22)		
Knowing and Using Number Facts	Explore, explain and recognise patterns of multiples in arrays of 20 and 32 teeth.	Ma2/2b
	Demonstrate multiplication as repeated addition.	Ma2/3a
Counting and Understanding Numbers	Understand the value of each digit in the price of an item on a shopping list.	Ma2/2c
Calculating	Identify and apply appropriate calculation methods to solve problems involving money.	Ma2/4a
Measuring	Use standard units of mass; convert grams to kilograms and vice versa in a variety of food products.	Ma3/4a
Handling Data	Represent discreet data through drawing graphs such as pictograms and bar charts to show preferences in favourite foods.	Ma4/2c
	Read and interpret graphs.	Ma4/2c
	Use data to create a class database about food.	Ma4/1f; ICT PoS 1b
	Use information held on the database to answer questions.	Ma4/1c; ICT PoS 1c

Teeth and Eating

Learning Objectives	Curriculum References
Design & Technology (Page 24)	
Evaluate a selection of commercially available sandwiches in terms of appearance, taste and cost.	PoS 5a; QCA Unit 3A
Discuss and note ideas prior to designing own sandwich, set success criteria.	PoS 1a-d
Use designs and plans to create a tortilla filling, following agreed food safety and hygiene procedures.	PoS 2a,f;5c
Assess the tortilla, gauge the opinion of others, identify successes and reflect on possible improvements.	PoS 3a-c
Design and assemble a suitable packaging item for the tortilla, using skills and techniques such as scoring and folding.	PoS 1c;2a,d,e;5b,c
Geography (Page 24)	
Make a study of a locality in the developing world, describe the environment and identify physical and human features.	PoS 3a,c,d,e
Recognise how the locality has connections with our own through the supply of goods.	PoS 3g
Collect evidence to demonstrate the far-reaching nature of the global food import and export industry.	PoS 1b
Art (Page 26)	
Investigate the work of artists who use images of food in their work.	PoS 4c;5d
Create a collection of starting points about food, ideas and observations.	PoS 1a-c;5a
Work on 2-D and 3-D projects to create sculptures and wall hangings featuring food, in large and small scale, both individually and collaboratively.	PoS 5b
PE (Page 26)	
Combine and sequence movements to produce a dance routine about the food journey.	PoS 6a
Music (Page 26)	
Learn, rehearse and perform songs about food.	PoS 1a-c
Explore, choose and use sounds to create musical effects for the food journey.	PoS 2a,b
History (Page 27)	
Explore dentistry at different times using a variety of source material.	PoS 4a
Use gathered information to answer questions about dentistry in the past.	PoS 4b
Sequence images and dental artefacts into correct time periods.	PoS 1a
RE (Page 27)	
Consider the role of charitable organisations in the distribution of food to less economically developed countries.	PoS 2e;3d
PSHCE (Page 27)	
Identify the role of food and eating in a healthy lifestyle.	PoS 3a
Recognise the importance of dental hygiene.	PoS 3a,b

Teeth and Eating

Science

Starting Points

- Look at and handle examples of real human teeth, such as 'milk teeth' from children or an extracted adult tooth.

- Look at a large-scale model of a set of human teeth.

- Make a study of the structure of a tooth; produce a large, labelled poster for classroom display.

- Investigate the four different types of human tooth (incisors, canines, pre-molars and molars) and their role in processing food in the mouth.

- Using a collection of real or 'play' food, ask the children to sort the items into two groups, foods which are good for and foods which are bad for our teeth. Ask the children to provide reasons for their decisions and choices.

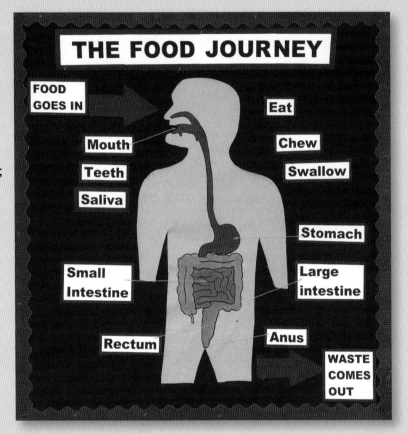

Enquiry

- Discuss the importance of both eating the correct foods and of effective toothbrushing in achieving good dental hygiene. Conduct a quick survey to determine which children have had fillings in their teeth. Talk about the causes of dental decay. Using pieces of eggshell as a comparable substitute for real teeth, investigate what occurs when the eggshell pieces are placed in containers holding liquids such as water, milk, orange juice, cola, and blackcurrant squash, and then left for 24 hours. Ask the children to predict the likely effects before testing and to identify which variables must stay the same in order to achieve as fair a test as possible. Use a digital camera to take 'before' and 'after' pictures. Ask the children to talk about what has happened and whether their predictions were correct. What conclusions can the children draw from this experiment? Can the children now think of a subsequent line of enquiry that can be tested? Use the activity sheet on page 19.

Extension Activities

- Explain that the teeth, tongue and saliva are only the first part of the digestive process and use a range of sources to explore the rest of the journey that food takes through the body, as shown on the display.

- Amazingly, the human stomach contains dilute hydrochloric acid to chemically break down food. Ask the children to find out why this potentially dangerous acid doesn't burn through the stomach lining and cause damage to the internal body cavity.

- Study the role of the different food groups in human nutrition. Sort foods into these groups.

- Make a 'food pyramid' display, with the foods that can be eaten occasionally placed at the top and the foods which can be eaten often at the bottom.

TOOTH TROUBLE

Teeth have a strong outer surface called enamel. Enamel can be eroded, leading to tooth decay. Using an eggshell in place of teeth, find out what happens to the shell when it is left for 24 hours in the following liquids:

water | milk | orange juice | fizzy cola

Draw what you observe after 24 hours have passed:

Eggshell left in water

Eggshell left in milk

Eggshell left in orange juice

Eggshell left in cola

NOW! Talk to a partner about what has happened.
Which liquid has caused the most damage and why?
Repeat the investigation with other liquids such as vinegar and tea.

Literacy

Speaking and Listening

- Hold a debate about healthy school dinners. Consider the points of view of the government, school caterers, parents, teachers and children.

- Form a 'conscience corridor' in the classroom. One side should try and persuade a volunteer to go ahead and eat sweets, the other side should aim to dissuade. Let a volunteer walk down the 'corridor', listening to the opposing arguments for and against. The volunteer should reflect upon what has been said and then make a final decision to indulge in sweets or not!

Reading and Writing

- Ask the children to write a letter to the tooth fairy, ask her where she keeps all the teeth she collects and what she uses them for.

- The children could imagine they are a piece of food in a stomach. They should write about the strange new environment they find themselves in and speculate about what is going to happen to them!

- Ask the children to pretend that they are responsible for their family's weekly shop at the supermarket. They should use bullet points to write a list of the foods that they would choose to buy.

- Ask the children to write or complete a fact sheet about teeth using the activity sheet on page 21.

- Read information texts about teeth such as *I know why I brush my teeth* by Kate Rowan (Walker Books) and *Teeth: a dentist's view* by Ian Park (Neate Publishing). Ask the children to make notes using key words and phrases and discuss the notes with others.

- Read fiction texts about eating such as *The big wide-mouthed frog* (see display above) by Ana Martin Larranaga (Walker books), *Mamba and the crocodile bird* by Francis Usher (Heinemann) and *The selfish crocodile* by Faustin Charles (Bloomsbury).

Open wide!

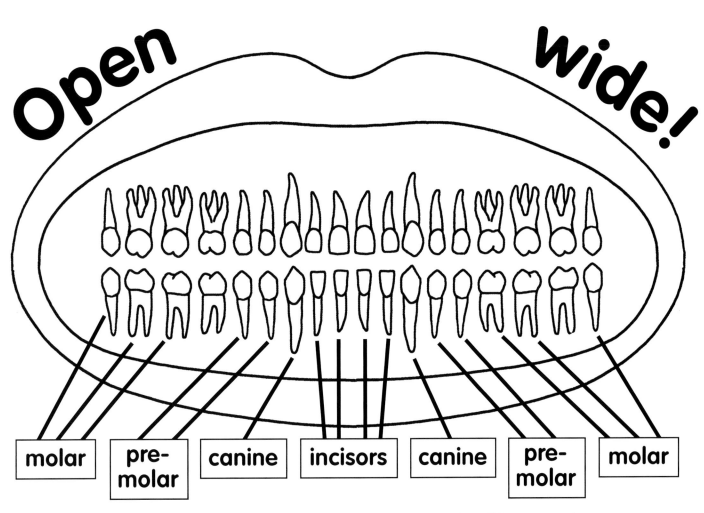

| molar | pre-molar | canine | incisors | canine | pre-molar | molar |

Read the text below. Complete the sentences by filling in the missing words shown in the bubbles below.

FACT BOX

Adults have thirty-two teeth, embedded in sockets in the

_____ bone and held in position by the

_____. The incisors have sharp edges for cutting, just

like a pair of _____. Canines are

_____ and are perfect for tearing food apart. The largest

teeth are called _____. These teeth

_____ and crush food until it is a soft lump, mixed

with _____, ready to be swallowed.

scissors — molars — jaw — saliva — pointed — grind — gums

Maths

Counting and Number Facts

- Use facts about the number of teeth that children (20) and adults (32) have to explore number patterns and arrays for multiples of 2, 4, 5, 8 and 10 (see the display and the activity sheet on page 23).

- Ask the children to use their knowledge of place value to sequence till receipts for food items into order from most expensive to the least expensive.

Calculating and Measuring

- Set up a 'mini mart' in the classroom and solve addition and subtraction problems using money. Use different written methods to find totals and calculate change.

- Arrange a selection of tinned and packet goods into the correct order according to weight, from lightest to heaviest.

- Ask the children to convert the weight of a food item from kilograms, such as a bag of sugar, into grams.

- Ask the children to find two or three lighter packaged food items which would together weigh the same as a heavier item.

Handling Data

- Draw a pictogram of the favourite sandwich fillings in your class.

- Make a bar graph to show the number of portions of fruit and vegetables that each child in the class has in a day. Work out the average number for the class as a whole.

- Decide upon and conduct a survey amongst the class or school to ascertain food preferences such as favoured crisp flavours, sandwich fillings, pizza toppings, favourite fruit or vegetables.

- Use the data gained from the survey to create a database. Make use of the information stored in the database, sharing it with relevant others such as school caterers or parents.

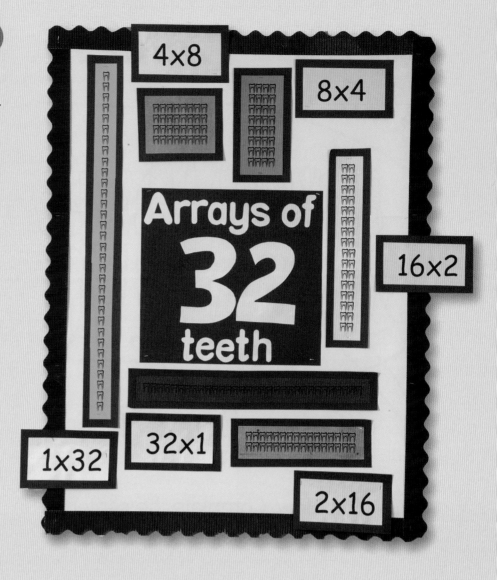

ARRAYS

Children have 20 teeth

 20 is a multiple of **2** **4** **5** and **10**

Draw the arrays for these multiplication facts:

4 X 5 = 20	**10 X 2 = 20**	**5 X 4 = 20**
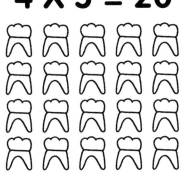		

Adults have 32 teeth

 32 is a multiple of **2** **4** and **8**

Draw the arrays for these multiplication facts:

4 X 8 = 32	**16 X 2 = 32**	**8 X 4 = 32**

How many more teeth do adults have than children?

•   Teeth and Eating   •   Belair Curricular-Links Science 3

Design & Technology

- Look at how ready-made sandwiches and snacks are packaged and marketed. Investigate popular fillings available in shops. Conduct a survey about favourite fillings amongst the class.

- Eat a sample of ready-made sandwiches or snacks and make comparisons between them such as in cost, taste or quality. Consider how sandwiches and snacks could be made healthier; highlight ingredients that could be replaced by a healthier option.

- Ask the children to discuss, design and make a healthy sandwich, baguette or tortilla wrap. Ask them to design and make packaging for the sandwich (see the activity sheet on page 25).

- Ask the children to imagine they are opening a new sandwich shop in the local area. Design and make a flyer to advertise the business. Consider how they would market the products on sale and create a demand for the sandwiches (see display).

Geography

- Investigate the 'food miles' the contents of a lunchbox or the toppings on a pizza from the local pizzeria have travelled. Just how 'local' is the pizza in reality?

- Ask each child to bring in five labels from canned produce and identify the country of origin. Find these places on a large map of the world. Consider the different stages of the journey that the produce has been on to end up in the kitchen cupboard.

- Find out as much as possible about the life of a farmer in a developing country, such as a banana grower in the Caribbean whose fruit is exported to be sold in the UK.

PRODUCT EVALUATION

I used these ingredients …

-
-
-
-
-

My tortilla tasted…

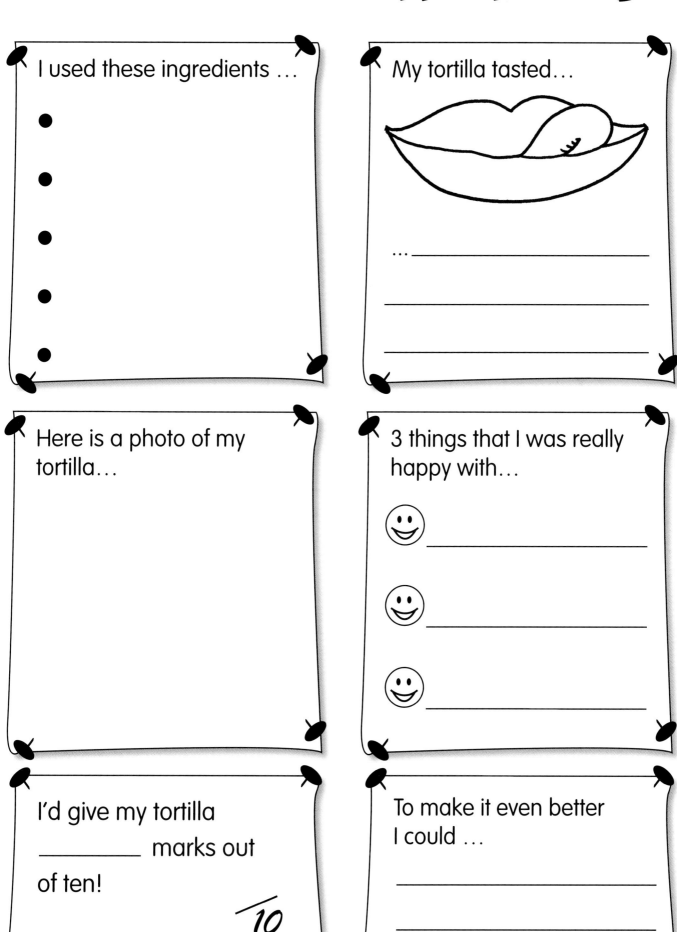

… _____

_____

_____

Here is a photo of my tortilla…

3 things that I was really happy with…

:) _____

:) _____

:) _____

I'd give my tortilla _____ marks out of ten!

/10

To make it even better I could …

_____

_____

• Teeth and Eating • Belair Curricular-Links Science 3

Art

- Create large-scale sculptures using food packaging or junk materials, to be displayed in the school, using the work of artists such as Antony Gormley (b. 1950) as a starting point.

- Use fabric paints to create a large-scale wall hanging about healthy eating featuring observational images of food.

- Use collage techniques to create a wall display featuring a plate of healthy food (see display above).

- Look at and recreate the work of Giuseppe Arcimboldo (1527–1593), creating portraits of class members using drawn or collaged images of fruit and vegetables.

- Photograph a piece of fruit at three stages such as an unripe, ripe and over-ripe banana and use the images to create a triptych.

- Look at Pop Art images of food by Andy Warhol (1928–1987) as a stimulus for creating own images, using a photocopier to enlarge or reduce and a selection of different coloured paper.

PE

- Working in small groups, rehearse and perform a dance interpreting the journey that food takes through the body.

Music

- Learn and sing songs such as *I'm a pink toothbrush* (by Max Bygraves, see www.6lyrics.com) and *Food, glorious food* from the musical *Oliver!*

- Explore how many different sound effects can be made using the lips, teeth and tongue.

- Explore the use of percussion instruments that could be used to create sound effects for the digestive journey, such as a rumbling tummy or teeth chewing food.

History

- Find out about the history of dentistry, from Roman times to the 21st century.

- Visit a dental museum such as the British Dental Association in London or the University of Liverpool Museum of Dentistry or download information from their websites: www.bda.org/museum and www.liv.ac.uk.

- Borrow a box of dental artefacts from an outreach service such as that run by the British Dental Association.

- Read extracts from information texts about the history of dentistry such as *The excruciating history of dentistry* by James Wynbrandt (St Martin's Press).

- Ask the children to write a page from the day book of an 18th-century dental surgeon; include lots of grim and gory details!

HOW TO KEEP YOUR TEETH CLEAN.

Wet your brush..then turn off the tap!

Squeeze the toothpaste on your brush

Brush your front teeth top and bottom

Brush your back teeth top and bottom

Rinse your mouth with water.

Put back your brush and floss.

RE

- Discuss the work of charitable organisations today that organise and supply food to those in need.

Rinse your mouth with water.

Squeeze the toothpaste on your brush

PSHCE

- Ask the children to keep a food and drink diary for a week, making note of the foods which are good and bad for their teeth.

- Ask the children to make a photo-story instruction leaflet or poster about how to look after their teeth (see display above).

- Hold a teethbrushing contest. Use disclosing tablets to discover who has been able to clean their teeth most effectively. Ensure you get parental permission first.

- Invite a dental nurse or dentist to come in and talk to the class about oral hygiene.

Properties of Materials

These grids demonstrate the learning objectives covered in the activities within the theme. The curriculum references indicate the relevant programme of study (PoS) for a subject area unless otherwise stated.

	Learning Objectives	Curriculum References
Science (Page 30)		
Scientific Enquiry	Review subject knowledge about insulation, develop questions to be explored and answered, gather information.	Sc1/2a,b; ICT PoS 1a
	Make predictions regarding outcomes.	Sc1/2c
	Plan and conduct a fair test investigation about insulation.	Sc1/2d,e
	Take measurements and collect evidence.	Sc1/2f
	Analyse and discuss results, drawing conclusions.	Sc1/2i,j,k
Materials and their Properties (QCA Science Unit 3C)	Observe and make comparisons between materials.	Sc3/1a
	Investigate the insulating properties of a range of materials, rank or sort materials into categories following testing.	Sc3/1b
	Measure the temperature of liquids.	Sc3/2c
Literacy (Page 32)		
Group Discussion and Interaction	Debate the use of fur in fashion, listen to and discuss opposing viewpoints appropriately.	En1/2e;3a
Creating and Shaping Texts	Develop and use interesting and engaging vocabulary about materials.	En3/1b
	Choose and use styles appropriate to poetry and non-fiction writing about materials.	En3/1a,d,e; ICT PoS 2a
Understanding and Interpreting Texts	Make notes and jottings about materials.	En3/9d
	Read a range of fiction and non-fiction texts about materials. Select information from texts, using organisational features effectively.	En2/3a,c,e
Mathematics (Page 34)		
Measuring	Use standard units of measurement for time, temperature and weight.	Ma3/4a
	Use appropriate measuring equipment.	Ma3/4b
	Read numbers accurately from a scale.	Ma3/4b
Understanding Shape	Recognise and continue a pattern made from shapes of different materials.	Ma3/2c
Handling Data	Present information in the form of a chart or table from an investigation about insulation.	Ma4/1f
	Use data to produce a graph.	Ma4/2c

Properties of Materials

Learning Objectives	Curriculum References
Design & Technology (Page 36)	
Evaluate a range of products.	PoS 3c;5a
Collect and develop design ideas for an egg cosy.	PoS 1a,b
Use a variety of tools and techniques to make an egg cosy.	PoS 2a,d;5c
Decorate and evaluate made articles.	PoS 2e;3c
RE (Page 36)	
Explore the biblical story of Joseph and his amazing coat.	PoS 1a;3a,f
Art (Page 38)	
Produce a quilt design using a variety of materials and processes.	PoS 5c
Develop ideas about pattern, shape and colour.	PoS 4a; ICT PoS 5b
Look at the work of painters and sculptors who use or portray unusual materials.	PoS 4c;5d; ICT PoS 1a;5b
Music (Page 38)	
Analyse sound effects made by different materials.	PoS 3a
Explore musical effects to create work.	PoS 3b
Rehearse and perform with percussion instruments.	PoS 1b,c
Geography (Page 39)	
Locate where materials come from on a globe or map.	PoS 2c
Provide reasons for the location of human development.	PoS 3d
Recognise how countries are linked through trade of materials.	PoS 3g
Consider the environmental impact of human activity on use of materials.	PoS 5a
History (Page 39)	
Identify change in the use of materials over a period of time.	PoS 2c
Engage in a study of a specific, significant period in British history and how materials were used then.	PoS 8a
PSHCE (Page 39)	
Raise environmental awareness of the overuse of plastic.	PoS 5a
Take responsibility for the environment.	PoS 5a
Make and act upon decisions.	PoS 2f

Properties of Materials

Science

Starting Points

- Introduce the word insulation and talk about everyday examples where materials are used to insulate, such as lagging around a hot water tank, a hot water bottle cover, a tea cosy used to keep the pot hot. Explain that insulation can refer to keeping cold things cold, as well as keeping hot things hot. A 'wine sleeve' is designed and used to keep chilled wine cold once it has been taken out of the fridge for example. It would be useful to illustrate this preliminary discussion with some of these items on hand.

Enquiry

- Explain the scenario of a rapidly cooling cup of tea on the teacher's desk (see the display above). Ask the children to suggest what could be done to prevent the tea from becoming cold too soon. Ask the children to select and test a variety of materials to see which one is the best at keeping a hot liquid at the hottest temperature over a period of time (see the activity sheet on page 31). Organise the children into small teams and ask each team to select one material to test. These could include bubble wrap, fabric, hay, wood shavings, cotton wool, shredded paper, sand and polystyrene chips. The teams should plan how to conduct the test using a container with hot but not boiling liquid. Make sure that the children understand that to ensure a fair test only one variable is being changed, and that is the type of insulating material being tested. Each team need a thermometer and must take the temperature of the liquid at the outset of the investigation and at regular intervals throughout the morning. There should be a 'control' sample, with no insulation, perhaps on the teacher's desk. This must have its temperature monitored at the same time as the children's samples. Children should record their temperature measurements on a chart or table. At the end of a given period, compare results and discuss the findings. Which material kept the liquid at the highest temperature by the end of the test period? Was this the same as expected?

Extension Activities

- Try the Ice Cube Challenge! Who can keep an ice cube in a frozen state for the longest period of time? Provide children with a selection of materials to get a discussion started and then give each child an ice cube to insulate in whichever manner they choose. Check the ice cubes at regular intervals throughout the day.

Insulation

Which material will provide the best insulation for a container of liquid?

Think about what you already know about the insulating properties of everyday materials.

CAUTION!

DO NOT USE BOILING HOT LIQUID!

Talk about the materials shown below. Predict which material you think will make the most effective insulator, keeping a hot liquid hot for a fixed time.

cotton wool

bubble wrap

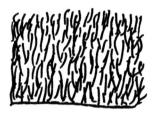

fur fabric

shredded paper

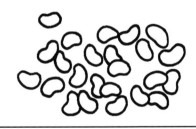

polystyrene chips

sand

You could try other materials too, such as wool, hay or sawdust.

How will you keep the test fair? Which things will you keep the same?

When you carry out the test, include a control sample with NO insulation.

Get all your equipment ready and carry out the investigation. Keep a careful note of times and temperatures.

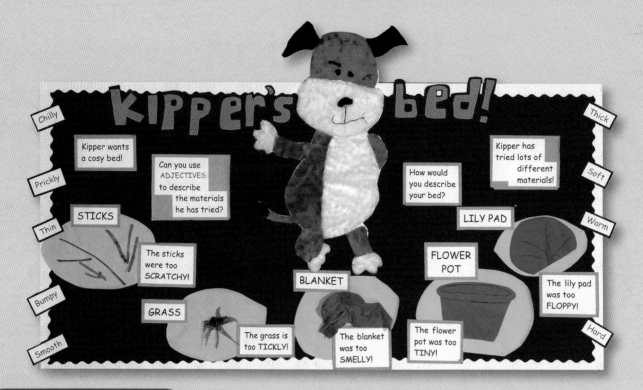

Literacy

Reading and Writing

- Read the story of *Kipper* by Mick Inkpen (Hodder Children's Books) and list the materials which Kipper tries out in his search for a comfortable, cosy bed. Ask the children to write a letter to Kipper in which they provide advice and suggestions as to how to go about buying a new bed. Perhaps they could invite Kipper to join you on a shopping trip.

- Collect adjectives that would be suitable for describing a bed, such as that shown on the activity sheet on page 33 (also see the display above). Ask the children to use the words as a stimulus for writing a poem about their bed. They should try to include elements of alliteration or simile, rhyme or repetition. Read the poems out aloud to see what they sound like as they draft them.

- Read non-fiction texts such as *Materials: their properties and uses* by David Byrne (Discovery World) and *Materials and their properties* by Angela Royston (Heinemann) and ask the children to make notes on key points.

- Create a class big book called Properties of Materials. Include organisational devices such as contents page, index, and glossary. Different groups of children could be assigned to produce different sections of the text.

- Display a selection of items made from one material, for example, woollen hats, gloves, scarves, jumpers and surround the items with descriptive language generated by the children as they handle the items.

- Use a visual image such as a striking piece of sculpture as a starting point for a poem. Ask the children to jot down words that immediately spring to mind when looking at and talking about the sculpture. Concentrate on the visual and tactile qualities of the materials used in the sculpture and the effect this produces. Sort words into categories and use as a vocabulary bank for a collaborative poem.

Speaking and Listening

- Is it ever acceptable to kill animals for their fur? Organise teams and hold a debate, arguing the case for and against.

Properties of Materials

zZZ MY LOVELY BED zZZ

Look at the adjectives on the cosy quilt. Add some more describing words of your own in the empty spaces.

snug, soft, cushiony, warm, cosy, comfort, tranquil, safe, peace, heat, thick, nest

Use these words as a starting point for a poem about your own bed. Think about how you will use…

rhyme   repetition   similie

alliteration   rythmn   pattern

NOW!   Talk through your ideas and write your poem.

Maths

Measuring

- Discuss standard units of measurement for measuring temperature. Practise reading numbers from the scale on a thermometer. Ask the children to talk about where they have seen references to temperature in everyday situations such as in a TV weather report or on their kitchen oven.

- Use gram and kilogram weights to determine the strength of plastic carrier bags. Record results in a table, converting all of the measurements into either grams or kilograms.

Shape

- Look at the pattern of rectangular shapes created by brickwork. Discuss why bricks are offset and not stacked on top of one another. Find other examples where shape and pattern are used for a particular purpose in construction both in the natural and man-made environment.

Handling Data

- Take recorded temperature readings from science investigations such as that shown on page 35 and organise the results into a table. Use the table of results to create a continuous data graph of temperature reduction over time (use the activity sheet on page 35). Display the graphs alongside the material tested as shown.

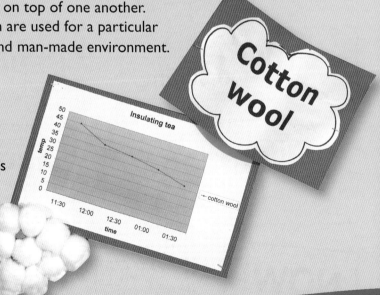

Properties of Materials

 # A lovely cup of tea!

 Helen used bubble wrap to insulate a container of tea. Here are her results.

TIME OF DAY	TEMPERATURE
9.30 am	45° C
10.00 am	38° C
10.30 am	31° C
11.00 am	38° C
11.30 am	26° C
12.00 noon	22° C

  Jenni used cotton wool balls to insulate a container of tea. Here are her results.

TIME OF DAY	TEMPERATURE
9.30 am	45° C
10.00 am	37° C
10.30 am	34° C
11.00 am	31° C
11.30 am	27° C
12.00 noon	24° C

 **Make a continuous data line graph for Helen or Jenni's results. Which material was the better insulator?**

Design & Technology

- Make a class collection of egg cosies. Look at the materials used and discuss whether they are suitable for the design purpose, that is, keeping a boiled egg warm by insulation. Look at the colours and designs used, are they attractive? Discuss preferences.

- Ask the children to draw a design idea for an egg cosy. They should annotate their drawing with remarks such as which stitching to use to join fabric together. Make a paper pattern, cut the fabric and assemble the egg cosy (see the activity sheet on page 37). Use a digital camera to keep a record of the work in progress.

- Embellish and decorate the egg cosy then try it out using some boiled eggs to eat. Remember to take great care with boiling water. Discuss how well the egg cosies work. Are they attractive to the eye? Have they met the design proposal?

- Try making a mug cosy, to keep a hot drink warm (see display above).

- Look at a range of other made products where certain materials have been used for their insulating properties, such as hot-water bottle covers made from thick fabric or wool. Conduct a consumer survey, gathering information about cost, size, design, and the materials used in hot-water bottle covers from a variety of retail outlets. Which item is actually the most efficient in keeping a bed warm?

- Look at foam containers or cool-boxes designed to keep canned drinks cold. Evaluate the effectiveness of the materials used.

- Hold a discussion about who has got the warmest coat in the class. Look at the range of materials used to make the coats and have a trying on session. The school playground can be a bitterly cold place in the winter months. Ask the children to draw a design, with annotations, of their ideal warm winter coat.

- The children could conduct a survey to find out what teachers wear to keep themselves warm on playground duty. Is there a most commonly used material?

RE

- Read the Bible story *Joseph and his amazing coat* by Heather Amery (Usborne). Discuss (a) the materials used in the coat, and (b) why Joseph was given this coat and what effect it had on the members of his family.

Properties of Materials

KEEP IT COSY

Here are some finished egg cosies.

humpty design

bear design

lion design

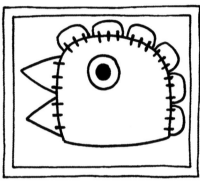
hen design

vampire design

face design

Design your own egg cosy here.
Think about …

- fabric

- colour

- style

- stitching

- decoration

- purpose

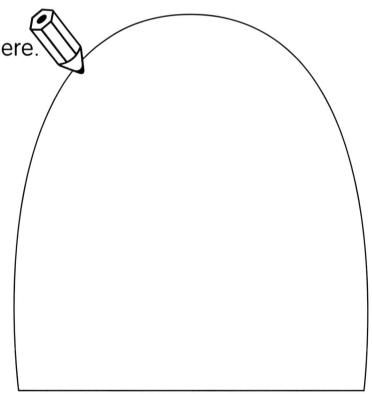

 **NOW!** | Make a paper pattern for your egg cosy.

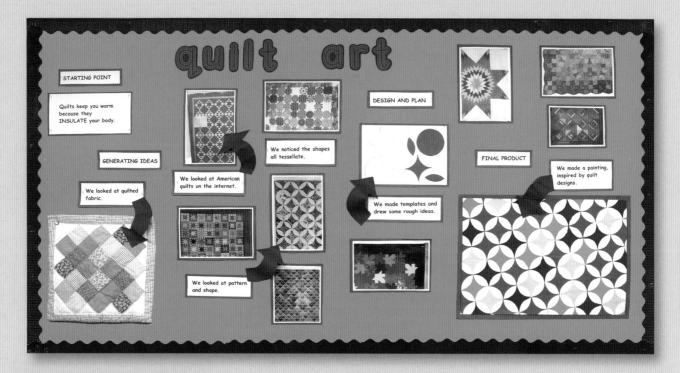

Art

- Look at a selection of quilted bedspread designs. Images of quilts can be obtained from the internet if you do not have access to actual artefacts to handle. Pay close attention to how colour, shape and pattern have been used to create the overall design. Look at repeated shapes and how tessellation has been used.

- Use quilt designs as a starting point for artwork featuring tessellating shapes and patterns (see display above).

- Use graphics software to design a pattern for a cosy quilted bedspread.

- Invite a guest into the class to give a knitting demonstration and to teach basic knitting stitches, then have a go at creating something knitted.

- Use clay to create work in 3-D. Look at how pottery has been used by other artists.

- Look at the painting *The persistence of memory* by Salvador Dalí (1908–1989), which features melting watches. Discuss the unsettling and disturbing effect of the materials in the painting behaving in an unexpected, unusual way.

- Look at an online image of the exploded shed installation *Cold dark matter: an exploded view* by Cornelia Parker (b. 1956) from www.tate.org.uk and discuss the effect of the shattered pieces of a wooden garden shed.

Music

- Ask the children to create a piece of music using items made from only one material, such as plastic, for example tapping and scraping plastic utensils to create sounds which could be put together to create a desired effect.

- Discuss and play instruments made from wood and metal and how these materials affect the quality of sound made by the instrument. The timbre of sound produced by a xylophone is very different for example to that of a glockenspiel.

Properties of Materials

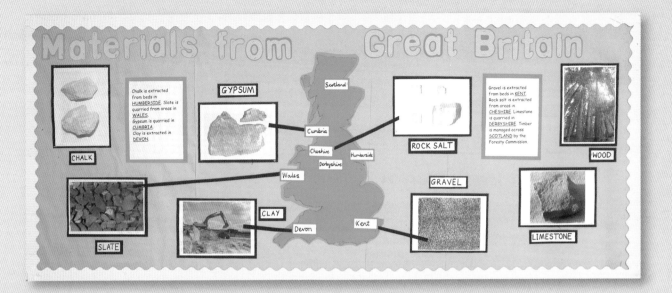

Geography

- Investigate how people from different countries around the world use materials to keep themselves warm or to keep cool. Look at the different fabrics used for clothing in various climates around the world or the materials used in insulating homes.

- Ask the children to research one material, such as the many different uses for bamboo in Asia. Find out about the properties of this material and why it is so important across this continent.

- Focus attention on the manufacturing industry based around one material such as steel or timber. Where are the major global locations for such industries? Which products are created from these raw materials and why? See the display above.

History

- Look at how the use of materials has changed over time with, for example, house building, clothing or the manufacture of toys.

- Look at the history of road building materials. Tarmac for example has been used for over one hundred years. Place significant developments on a time line.

- Research the life and work of a famous scientist from the past whose work included investigating the properties of materials, such as Isaac Newton (1642–1727) or Michael Faraday (1791–1867).

- Investigate a specific period in British history, such as the Anglo-Saxons, and focus on how and why materials were selected and used. You could concentrate on one specific area such as metalworking.

PSHCE

- Find out how many plastic bags are given away by a supermarket chain in one year. Hold a debate to discuss whether it is any longer acceptable for us to use plastic bags from shops given that we know that the plastic will take many years to rot down. Talk about alternatives to plastic carrier bags such as those made from hessian or cotton and why these materials are more environmentally friendly.

- Ask the children to find out how much plastic waste is thrown away by their family in just one week. Contact the local council to see whether a plastic recycling facility exists in your area and, if not, challenge them to provide an explanation for this omission.

Helping Plants Grow

These grids demonstrate the learning objectives covered in the activities within the theme. The curriculum references indicate the relevant programme of study (PoS) for a subject area unless otherwise stated.

	Learning Objectives	Curriculum References
Science (Page 42)		
Scientific Enquiry	Collect evidence about plants through measurement and observation, to test ideas.	Sc1/1b;2f
	Create a fair test by changing one variable.	Sc1/2d
	Make comparisons and draw conclusions from findings.	Sc1/2i,j
Life Processes and Living Things (QCA Science Unit 3B)	Understand the effects of different factors on plant growth.	Sc2/3a
	Understand the role played by plant parts such as roots and leaves.	Sc2/3b,c
	Understand plant life processes include growth, nutrition and reproduction.	Sc2/1b
Literacy (Page 44)		
Speaking	Present a timed talk about plants using specific vocabulary.	En1/1a
Understanding and Interpreting Texts	Make notes of the key words used in a piece of text about plants.	En2/3c; En3/1a
	Read information texts about plants.	En2/3a,e
	Create a plant vocabulary bank.	En2/3c; En3/1b
Creating and Shaping Texts	Plan and write stories, poems and information texts about plants for different audiences.	En3/1c;2a,b
	Include imaginative and creative ideas in own fiction writing.	En3/9a
	Use detail in instructions and information texts about how to care for a plant.	En3/9b
Mathematics (Page 46)		
Measuring	Correctly use and understand units of length and capacity.	Ma3/1a;4a
	Measure plant growth using suitable equipment.	Ma3/4b
	Measure quantities of liquid using appropriate equipment.	Ma3/4b
	Measure the perimeter of leaf shapes.	Ma3/4e
Understanding Shape	Alter position of leaves using rotation, translation and reflection.	Ma3/3b
	Tessellate shapes.	Ma3/2b
Handling Data	Collect data about plants and display using tables, graphs and charts.	Ma4/1f;2c; ICT PoS 2a
	Understand the difference between continuous and discreet data.	Ma4/2e

Learning Objectives	Curriculum References
Geography (Page 48)	
Use atlases and globes to locate types of plants around the world.	PoS 2c
Communicate and share information about plants in the locality.	PoS 1e; ICT PoS 3a
Link local flora with local conditions such as soil type.	PoS 3d; Sc2/1a
Consider how human activity can alter the local or global environment for plants.	PoS 4b;5a
PSHCE (Page 48)	
Consider the well-being, thoughts and feelings of others.	PoS 4a
Recognise the benefits of eating fruit and vegetables.	PoS 3a
Discuss the effects of medicinal plants on health and well-being.	PoS 3d
Art (Page 50)	
Draw plants from first hand observation.	PoS 1a;2c
Communicate ideas about colour and texture.	PoS 2c;4a
Experiment with processes such as dyeing.	PoS 4b
RE (Page 50)	
Compile and compare how flowers are used in religious festivals and celebrations.	PoS 1b;3g
Music (Page 50)	
Compose and sing songs about plants growing.	PoS 1a
Consider how a venue may affect a performance.	PoS 4d
History (Page 51)	
Undertake a study about the Romans and their use of plants (QCA unit 6A).	PoS 8a;9
Research famous historical figures, such as Capability Brown.	PoS 1a;2a
Design & Technology (Page 51)	
Make vegetable soup, following hygiene procedures.	PoS 2f;5c
Make gardening gloves using textiles.	PoS 5c
Evaluate commercially available and own products.	PoS 5a
PE (Page 51)	
Create and play invasion games.	PoS 7a
Take part in outdoor and adventurous activities.	PoS 11a,b

Science

Starting Points

- Ask the children to find out information about plants from online sources such as the Kew Gardens website at www.kew.org or by making a visit to a plant nursery, garden centre, local allotment or community parks and gardens.

- Establish the children's current knowledge about plants by briefly discussing work covered in previous years.

We pulled the leaves off of this plant. We noticed the plant growing some new leaves; the bud was shrivelled up and dying.

Enquiry

- The children will probably be aware that plants need roots and leaves in order to grow well and be able to produce new plants. Ask the children to think of a way of proving that this is the case. Introduce four healthy, identical potted plants, such as chrysanthemums, into the classroom. Site them together in the classroom so that all four plants have equal access to warmth and light and provide each plant with the same amount of water (see the activity sheet on page 43). Allow the children to observe that all four plants are growing healthily. Then, remove all the leaves from one plant, remove all the roots from one plant and remove all the flowers from one plant. Keep one plant in its original condition and explain to the children the idea of keeping a control sample. Ask the children to predict what they think will happen to each plant over the course of time. They may like to use a digital camera to record images, make sketches and write notes on the condition of each plant. At the end of a given period, such as two or three weeks, ask the children to look at the plants again and to consider the evidence that they have been collecting over the observation period. Do the observations prove or disprove the idea that plants need features such as roots and leaves in order to grow well?

Extension Activities

- Look at the claims made in the advertising of plant food, for example in a gardening magazine. Introduce two identical potted flowering plants into the classroom and keep them in identical conditions. Add liquid plant food to the water of one plant but not the other over a period of time and observe any differences that occur in the health and growth of the plants.

What do plants really need?

You will need four identical potted flowering plants for this investigation.

1 **Plant 1.** Remove ALL the leaves.

NO LEAVES

2 **Plant 2.** Remove ALL the roots. Then return the plant to the pot.

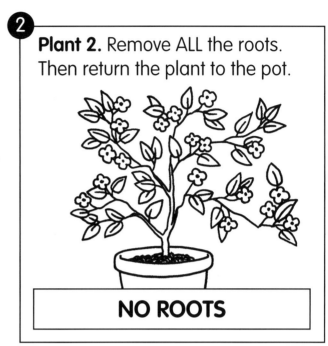

NO ROOTS

3 **Plant 3.** Remove ALL the flowers.

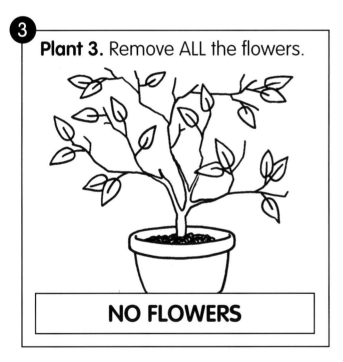

NO FLOWERS

4 **Plant 4.** Remove nothing.

CONTROL

Keep the plants together in a warm, sunny place. Give them all the same amount of water. Observe what happens to the plants over two weeks. After two weeks make a final assessment.

NOW! Which of the four plants can:
Make their own food? Produce seeds? Uptake water?
Discuss your ideas with a friend.

Literacy

Speaking and Listening

- Ask the children to prepare and present a one minute talk to the class about a plant of their choice, using appropriate vocabulary.

IMAGINE A PLANT

My plant is a MAGICAL plant. When you touch it it will burst out a GOLDEN SPICKY knife. When you run, it will spring out a dazzling trap. When you drive past the fabulous plant you will see a CRAZY flower. If you look very closely, you will see lots of hairs.

By Harry J and Jordan K

Imagine a plant

The plant has leaves like hands with rings on every finger. A prickly thorn with very sharp ends come of the stem. Golden leaves with the golden rules written on. A little mini pink t-shirt, two wings so it look's like a bird, two teeth so it can talk and one eye so it can see. Some hair so it feels soft. A psp in his hand so he isn't bord. The plant grows sweets to make it looks better.

By Bradley and Tommy

Reading and Writing

- Read non-fiction texts such as *Plants* (Factfinders) by Andrew Charman (BBC books).

- Use an artefact such as an old, well-worn gardening tool as the starting point for planning and writing a story.

- Ask the children to write the recipe for a plant-based potion that could be used by a character such as Harry Potter. Remember to include written advice on the effects that the potion will have!

- Ask the children to use the worksheet on page 45 to plan a poem or a piece of descriptive text about an imaginary plant that they have grown or come across in an outdoor space (see display above).

- Make a visit to a public garden or park or a plant centre, taking notes about the colours, textures and smells that you encounter. Ask the children to use the notes to compile a report entitled 'In praise of plants!' They should use paragraphs to organise the text.

- Create a vocabulary resource display about plants in the shape of a tree, with each leaf adorned with a word.

- Write calligrams using plant-related vocabulary such as stem, flower, root, leaf, stalk, twig, trunk or branch.

- The children could write some instructions, designed perhaps for a younger child, about how to care for a houseplant or grow a plant from seed.

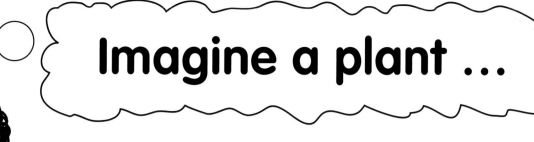

Imagine a plant ...

Those strange little seeds that you found and planted last month have grown into a weird and wonderful plant.

What does your plant look like, feel like, smell like, taste like and sound like? Fill in the bullet points below:

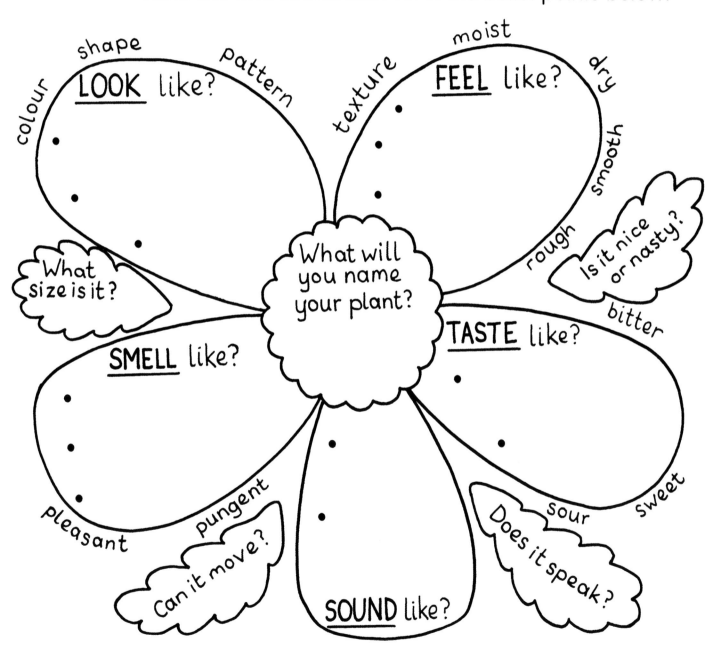

NOW!   Use your ideas and key words to write a descriptive poem about your plant.

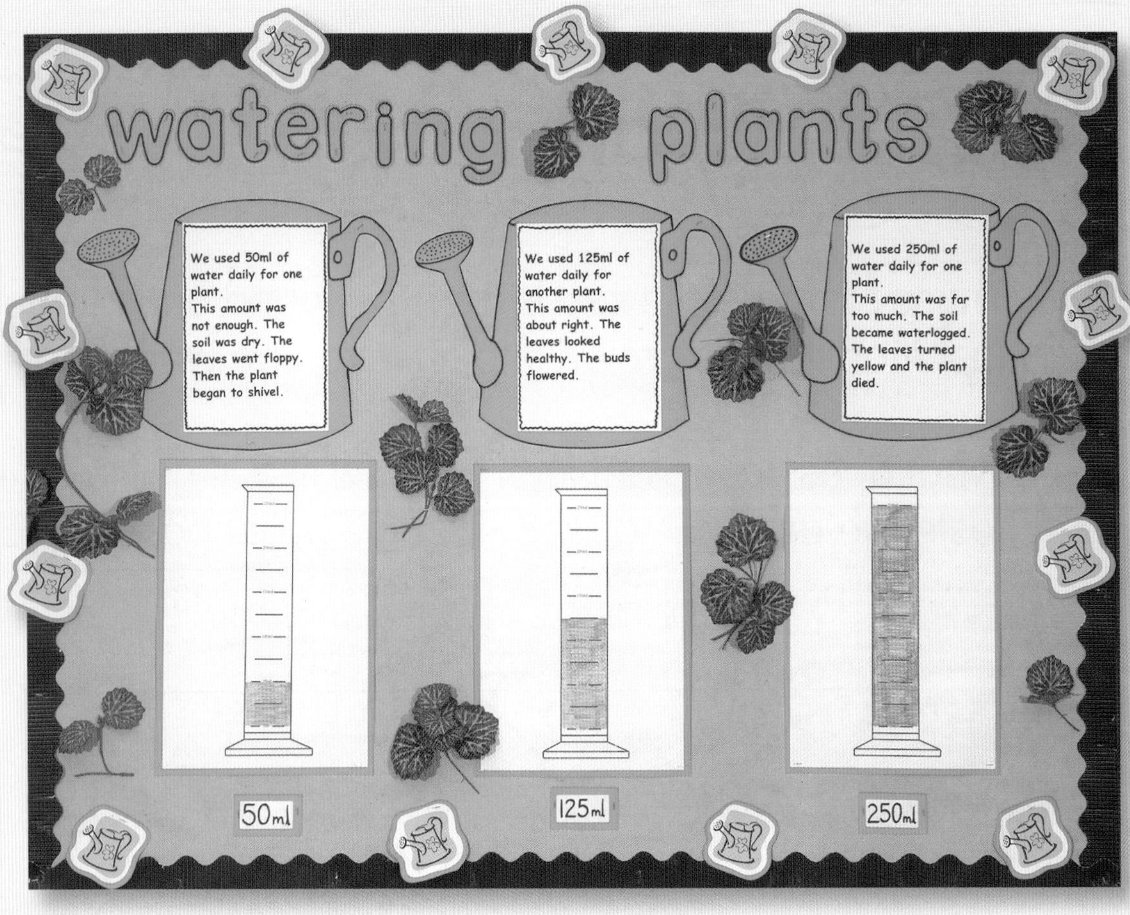
watering plants
We used 50ml of water daily for one plant. This amount was not enough. The soil was dry. The leaves went floppy. Then the plant began to shivel.
We used 125ml of water daily for another plant. This amount was about right. The leaves looked healthy. The buds flowered.
We used 250ml of water daily for one plant. This amount was far too much. The soil became waterlogged. The leaves turned yellow and the plant died.
50ml
125ml
250ml

Maths

Measuring

- Draw around a variety of leaves on squared paper and calculate their area.
- Use the context of watering plants in the classroom as a means of revising work on capacity. Ask the children to measure out exact quantities of water using measuring jugs, cylinders and syringes (see the display above). Introduce the idea of ratio and proportion when adding a quantity of liquid plant food to an amount of water.
- Ask the children to measure the perimeter of leaves using string. Record and compare the lengths.

Understanding Shape

- Ask the children to create a tessellating leaf shape on squared paper.
- Use leaf images to conduct work on the rotation, reflection and translation of shapes.

Handling Data

- Organise and sort a selection of leaves using a Carroll diagram.
- Measure the growth of a quick-growing plant over a period of time and record the data in a table. Use the information to produce a continuous line graph (see the activity sheet on page 47).
- Conduct a survey within the school to find out which garden plant is the most popular. Ask the children to think of ways to collect and organise the information for themselves and to consider how they could present the information.
- Ask the children to investigate a question such as *'Do flowers all have the same amount of petals?'* Ask the children to collect evidence and present results graphically or in a table.

Measuring growth

Plant a quick-growing bulb such as an amaryllis. As soon as a shoot emerges, measure its growth over a two-week period and record the data on this chart:

Day 1 cm	Day 2 cm	Day 3 cm	Day 4 cm	Day 5 cm	Day 6 cm	Day 7 cm
Day 8 cm	Day 9 cm	Day 10 cm	Day 11 cm	Day 12 cm	Day 13 cm	Day 14 cm

Now use the information to create a continuous line graph to show growth over time.

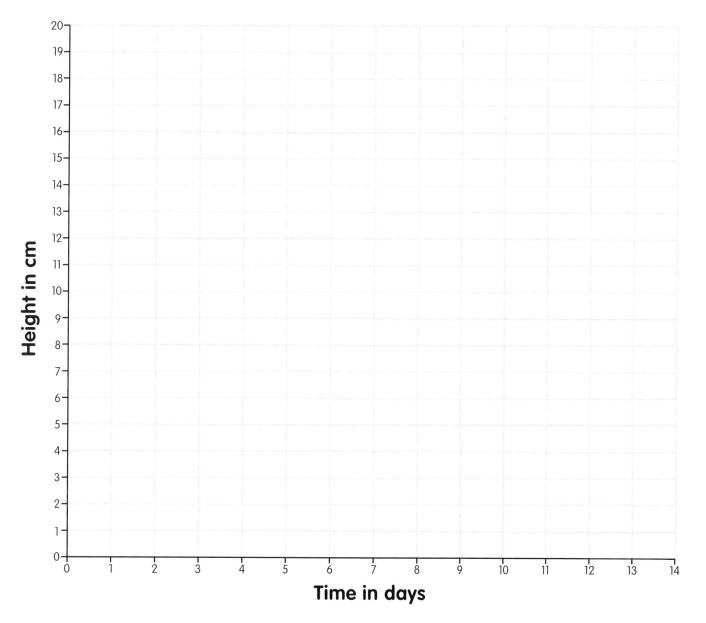

Geography

- Investigate the correlation between types of soil and the types of native plants that occur. For instance, which kinds of flowering plants grow on chalk grassland? Compare the children's findings with another geographical area in the UK, such as plants that occur on sand dunes, on shingle beaches or in a pine forest.

- Create a classroom display showing the different types of plant that can be found in different locations around the world. Ask the children to consider how plants are adapted to survive in the growing conditions and climate in which they can be found (see the activity sheet on page 49).

- Talk about the positive environmental effects that plants have on a local scale, such as plant roots stabilising the soil on a slope and preventing soil erosion.

- Discuss how human activity can cause negative environmental changes, such as with air pollutants falling as acid rain and killing Scandinavian forests and illegal logging activity destroying forests in South East Asia.

PSHCE

- Plants and flowers are often given as gifts or to express feelings. Show the children an attractive bouquet of flowers. How would they feel if they were given these as a gift? Can they name someone that they would give such a gift to? How would it make them feel and why? Hold a discussion on the subject of the power of plants. Consider whether plants can alter our mood and influence our feeling of well-being.

- Discuss the many medicinal properties of plants. Salic acid in aspirin, for instance, comes from the bark of willow trees. Plant products such as tea tree oil have antiseptic properties and certain flowers such as lavender and chamomile are renowned for their soothing and relaxing effects.

- Discuss the promotion of the current 'five-a-day' recommendation for the daily intake of fruit and vegetables. Are such schemes necessary and if so why?

PLANTS AROUND THE WORLD

Where do these plants come from? Find their locations on a globe or world map. Write them down.

PLANT		LOCATION
	bamboo	
	oak	
	cacti	
	pampas	
	baobab	
	rubber tree	
	olive	
	pine tree	
	mangrove	

 **Talk to a friend about the reasons why there are different plants in different locations.**

Art

- Choose some striking flowers from a florist's and ask the children to create large-scale, dramatic images of the blooms using pastels or paint. Then as a direct comparison choose a delicate flower such as a sweet pea and ask the children to make observational drawings then add gentle watercolour washes to the pencil outlines.

- Attach plant items collected from the school grounds to a strip of card to create a natural colour 'palette'.

- Make a natural colours display like the one shown here. Begin with squares of plain calico and use a variety of fruits and vegetables as a natural dye. For instance, soak one calico square in a bowl of beetroot, place another in a saucepan containing chopped onions, skins left on, and water. Simmer this and leave the fabric square in the resulting liquid overnight. Try the same technique with cabbage leaves. Squish a can of chopped tomatoes onto a fabric square and leave overnight. You could also ask the children to think about which foods stain their clothes easily, then try those items on the fabric squares too.

natural colours

We've been experimenting with natural food dyes.

We began with pieces of plain white cotton fabric.

beetroot

Beetroot juice turned the fabric a lovely shade of pink!

onion

Boiled onion skins made this pale brown colour.

cabbage

Cabbage dye created this pale green colour.

tomato

This orange colour was produced with tomato juice.

RE

- Talk about how plants and flowers are used in religious ceremonies, for example a bride carrying a bouquet, a church or synagogue being decorated at harvest time, floral tributes at a funeral.

- Investigate which plants and flowers are mentioned in religious texts and find out whether certain plants or flowers have symbolic meaning.

tomato

This orange colour was produced with tomato juice.

Music

- It is often said that gardeners talk to their plants to encourage them to grow. Ask groups of children to write and sing a song, either set to a popular tune or to their own original score, to be sung as encouragement for plants to grow. Sing the songs to plants growing in your classroom!

- Plan and hold a 'garden party' concert in your school garden or wildlife area. Ask the children to consider how the outdoor venue will influence the choice of music to be played.

Text visible on display:

How the ROMANS used PLANTS

FODDER
BEDDING
BUILDING
FABRIC

MEDICINES
DYEING
FOOD AND DRINK

Cereals such as BARLEY were grown as animal fodder.

ROSE petals were placed inside pillows.

ROSEMARY and WORMWOOD were used for medicinal purposes.

FLAX was grown to make linen for clothing.

They used OLIVE OIL to make soap.

They believed eating GARLIC made them strong.

They used LAVENDER to scent their bath water.

History

- Investigate the use of dendrochronology, the method of counting the rings found in a cross section of a tree trunk in order to ascertain the age of the tree.

- Enquire into the work of famous landscape gardeners from the past, such as Capability Brown (1716–1783). Visit www.capability-brown.org.uk as a source of information.

- Research the different ways in which people from a period in history, for instance the Romans, used plants in their everyday lives. Create a display such as the one shown above.

Design & Technology

- Make a vegetable soup from vegetables and herbs grown in the school vegetable patch. Serve the soup for lunch! Taste-test a range of canned vegetable soups, in comparison with the fresh, home-made soup.

- Ask the children to make sketches for a sensory garden for a visually-impaired person.

- Evaluate a range of gardening gloves. Ask the children to consider how effective the gloves would be, for example at keeping your hands clean or preventing being stung by nettles or pricked by thorns. Ask the children to design and make a new pair of gardening gloves using a material of their choice. Test the finished gloves in the school garden.

- Design a logo for the school gardening club. Create badges using the logo or use stencils and fabric paints to embellish plain white t-shirts with the design.

PE

- Ask groups of children to make up a plant-themed invasion game that can be played in small teams. For instance the two opposing teams could be 'cabbage leaves' and 'slugs'.

- Get the children out and about in the school grounds by developing a trail or orienteering activity.

- Revive the tradition of maypole dancing in your school as a celebration of spring.

Light and Shadow

These grids demonstrate the learning objectives covered in the activities within the theme. The curriculum references indicate the relevant programme of study (PoS) for a subject area unless otherwise stated.

	Learning Objectives	Curriculum References
Science (Page 54)		
Scientific Enquiry	Discuss the cause and effect of shadows and obtain evidence through testing.	Sc1/1a,b
	Make observations and measurements of shadows. Communicate findings through drawings, photographs and tables.	Sc1/2f,h
	Identify and explain patterns in observations made. Discuss and draw conclusions from data.	Sc1/2i,j,l
Physical Processes (QCA Science Unit 3F)	Investigate light sources and their everyday effects including shadows and reflections. Identify materials that are transparent, translucent and opaque.	Sc4/3a,b,c; Sc3/1a
	Investigate the transit of the sun across the sky during the day and the effect this has on light and shadows.	Sc4/4b
Literacy (Page 56)		
Speaking	Read riddles about shadows to an audience.	En1/1a,b;8a
Drama	Create and present a play performed by puppets.	En1/4b;8b;11b
Understanding and Interpreting Texts	Identify the key points about light and shadows from information texts.	En2/3a,c
Engaging with and Responding to Texts	Read a variety of stories around the theme of light and shadows.	En2/4c;8a
	Identify how atmosphere is developed through setting, character and plot.	En2/4c
	Review a story, comment on the language used by the author.	En3/9a,c,d
Creating and Shaping Texts	Plan and write stories, poems and riddles.	En3/1a;2a-e
	Use the format of known stories as the basis for own composition.	En3/1d
	Write a playscript for shadow puppet performance.	En3/12
Mathematics (Page 58)		
Calculating	Use addition or subtraction to calculate the difference between largest and shortest shadow length.	Ma2/3a
Measuring	Choose and use standard units of measurement.	Ma3/4a
	Correctly use units of time.	Ma3/4d
	Record measurements of shadows accurately.	Ma3/4b
	Find the perimeter of irregular shapes.	Ma3/4e

Light and Shadow

Learning Objectives	Curriculum References
History (Page 60)	
Find out about people such as Sir Isaac Newton from a variety of sources.	PoS 4a; ICT PoS 1a;5b
Use the correct vocabulary associated with chronology and time pieces.	PoS 1a,b
Research the customs and beliefs of an ancient civilisation such as the Egyptians.	PoS 13
PE (Page 60)	
Respond to musical stimuli as a starting point for a shadow dance.	PoS 6b
Create and perform shadow dances with a partner.	PoS 6a
PSHCE (Page 60)	
Recognise and suggest responses to risk associated with being in the dark or in poor light scenarios.	PoS 3e
Ask and answer questions of a road user.	PoS 5e
Geography (Page 62)	
Use a globe, maps and plans to locate places in different time zones.	PoS 2c
Obtain information about Greenwich Mean Time from a variety of sources.	PoS 2d; ICT PoS 5b
Art (Page 62)	
Draw shadows from observation.	PoS 1a
Consider visual elements of light and colour.	PoS 4a
Evaluate the work of artists such as J. M. W. Turner.	PoS 4c
RE (Page 63)	
Discuss the symbolism of light in a variety of religions.	PoS 1d
Understand the use of light and the specialness of a place of worship.	PoS 1b;2a;3a-c
Design & Technology (Page 63)	
Evaluate the properties of materials used to create high visibility clothing.	PoS 4a
Design and make a high-visibility item from textiles.	PoS 1a-c;2d;5c
Test that the item meets its purpose.	PoS 3c
Music (Page 63)	
Sing songs with a theme of light.	PoS 1a
Use a non-musical stimulus featuring light as a starting point for composition.	PoS 2b;5b
Record own music.	PoS 5d; ICT PoS 3a

Light and Shadow

Science

Starting Points

● What is a shadow? Ask the children to discuss this question in groups and then share ideas together. Create an agreed class definition of a shadow. Display the definition alongside a display of photographs of shadows taken with a digital camera around the school grounds or add the shadow definition to a class-made science dictionary.

Enquiry

● Conduct a shadow stick investigation (see the activity sheet on page 55). Secure a large circle of plain white paper into the ground using a pencil, a sturdy stick or piece of dowel pushed through the centre of the paper and securely into the ground. Record by drawing on the white paper circle the position and length of the shadow made by the upright stick at 9am. Ask the children to predict what will happen to the shadow in terms of its position and its length as the day progresses. Return to the stick every hour throughout the day and continue to record, by drawing on the paper circle, the shadow made by the stick. By 3pm the children should have an hour-by-hour record of the shadow clearly showing a shortening during the morning followed by a lengthening in the afternoon. At the end of the day, ask the children to use a ruler to measure the shadow markings and create a table of results. Allow time for the children to talk about what has happened and why. Encourage them to include understanding from their background knowledge, for instance about the apparent movement of the sun across the sky, when drawing conclusions about evidence collected.

Extension Activities

● Create a classroom wall display entitled 'Science Super Heroes' (see the display above), in which the phenomena of light, reflection and shadow are represented in the guise of 'super heroes'. Include factual captions as part of the display.

● Do all objects have a shadow? Discuss the difference between transparent, translucent and opaque objects and materials.

SHADOW STICK INVESTIGATION

You will need:

- a pencil or sharpened stick

- a large circle of plain white paper

What to do:

On a sunny day, push the pencil through the centre of a circle of paper into the ground. mark on the paper the position/length of the shadow

PREDICT:

What will happen to the position of the shadow?

PREDICT:

What will happen to the length of the shadow?

Check your shadow stick every hour throughout the day. Mark the position and length of the shadow on the paper using a pencil or pen.

 **NOW!** Talk with a friend about what has happened. Was it what you expected?

Literacy

Speaking and Listening

● Ask groups of children to produce a script for a shadow-puppet play. This could be accomplished by turning a well known story into a play script or by asking the children to produce an original piece. Rehearse and perform the plays, using bought or own-made puppets, to an audience.

● Write a riddle about a shadow. Ask the children to read out their riddles to another class and see if they can guess what is being described from the cryptic clues.

Reading and Writing

● Read fiction texts featuring light and shadows, such as *Oscar and the moth* by Geoff Waring (Walker books) *The bear under the stairs* by Helen Cooper (Corgi) and *I want my light on* by Tony Ross (Anderson Press).

● Ask the children to write a book review about a story they have read. Encourage them to think about the language that the author has employed to create effects and reactions.

● Use the story *The bear under the stairs* as a starting point for writing a similar story about a dark place such as under the bed. Talk about how a child's fear of the dark, combined with a vivid imagination, could lead to a climax in the story which is then resolved when a light source reveals the actual situation. (See the display above.)

● Read and discuss information texts such as *Light and dark* by Sally Hewitt (Franklin Watts), *Start up science: light and dark* by Claire Llewellyn (Evans Brothers) and *Light and shade* by Susanna Daniel (Longman books). Make notes of the key points of information, for instance by sticking brightly coloured labels on parts of the text.

● Create a science dictionary to which science vocabulary and definitions can be added to throughout the year.

● Use the shadowy stories activity sheet on page 57 as a starting point for writing an atmospheric story involving shadows and suspense.

● Write an acrostics poem, starting each new line with the initial letter from the word 'shadow'.

● Write calligrams using words such as shadow, bright, sparkle, gloom, dusk and shine.

SHADOWY STORIES

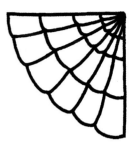

Pick a setting for your story:

A dark, spooky cellar under an old house

A gloomy attic full of cobwebs

A dim, musty cupboard under the stairs

A shadowy, abandoned house

Pick an object:

- a torch

- an old key

- a horseshoe

- damp matches

- a lantern

- a map showing underground tunnels

Pick a character:

- yourself

- a brave, fearless child

- a mysterious stranger

- a sad, elderly person

- an inquisitive little dog

- a teenager

NOW!

Write an exciting opener for your story.

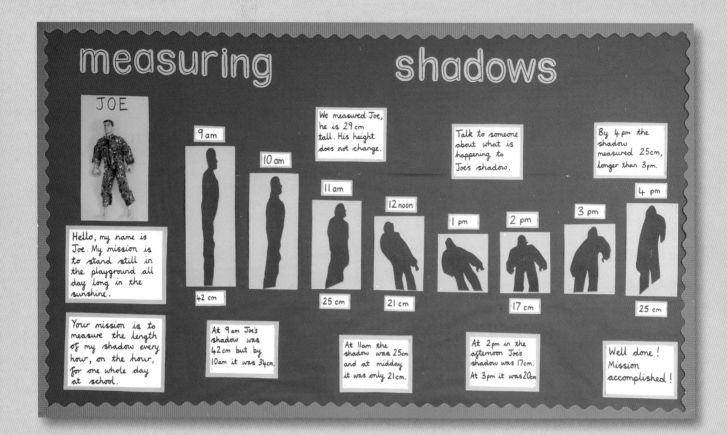

Maths

Calculating

● Ask the children to calculate the difference between the shortest and longest shadow length in the measuring shadows activity (see the activity sheet on page 59, also see the display above).

● Find out how many hours of sunlight are experienced on the shortest day (21st December) and the longest day (21st June) of the year and ask the children to calculate the difference between the two times in hours and minutes.

Measuring

● Practise the skill of accurate measuring with a ruler.

● Use a ruler or tape measure to measure the changing length of shadows created by inanimate objects left in the sunshine, such as a toy. Create a display of the shadows, clearly highlighting the change in the length of the shadow throughout the course of the day.

● Ask the children to work in pairs, drawing around their own shadow on the playground. Use a long length of string to measure the perimeter of the shadows.

● Revise work on time, including days, weeks, months, seasons. Look at www.greenwichmeantime.co.uk to view a global time zone chart. Ask the children to calculate the time difference between different countries using the chart as a reference point.

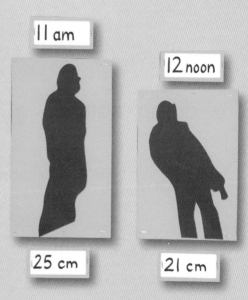

Shadows

Use a ruler to measure the length of these shadows.

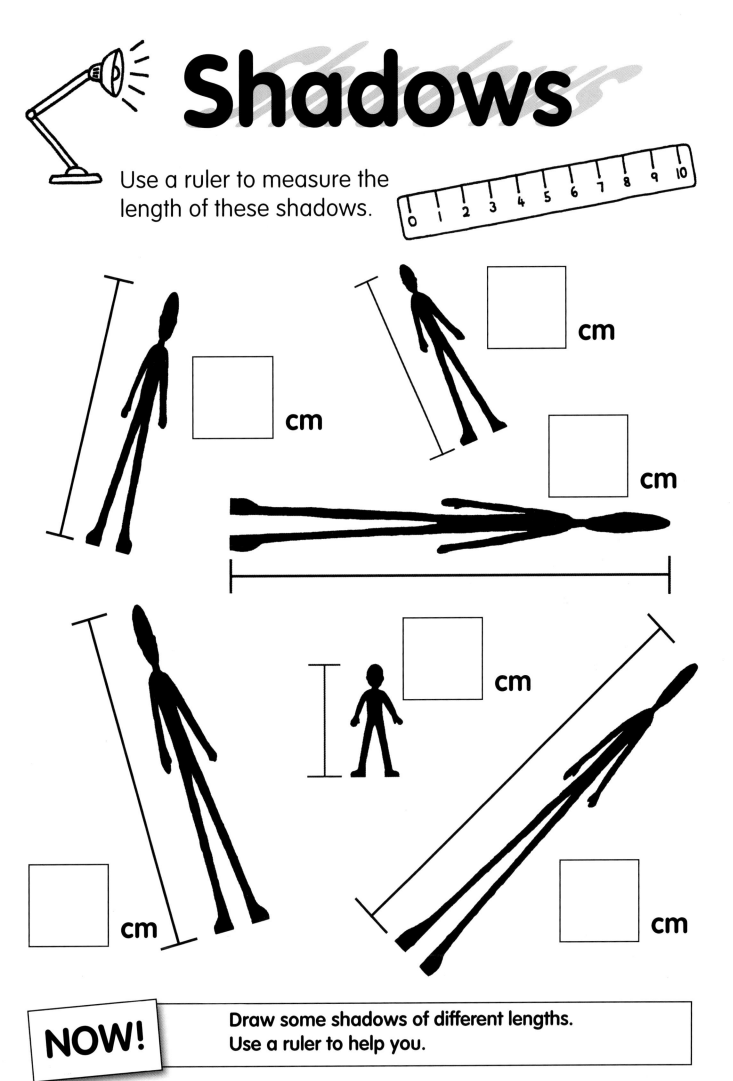

cm

cm

cm

cm

cm

cm

NOW! Draw some shadows of different lengths. Use a ruler to help you.

A sundial works by casting a shadow onto a fixed, flat surface, marked with the hours of the day.

Sundials utilize the perceived movement of the sun across the sky to tell the time.

History

- Use the Internet to research information about sundials. Ask the children to prepare and present a short talk about sundials focusing on key points or interesting facts (see display above).

- Use the activity sheet on page 61 to order images of timepieces in the correct chronological sequence.

- Read *The light bulb* (Fact finders: Great Inventions) by Marc Tyler Nobleman (Capstone Press) as a starting point for investigating the life and work of Thomas Edison (1847–1931).

- Conduct a research project about a famous scientist from the past, such as Sir Isaac Newton (1642–1727), who published his first paper on light in 1672.

- Find out about the worship of the sun in ancient civilisations such as the Egyptians, Aztecs or Romans.

- Visit the Royal Observatory at Greenwich or the National Maritime Museum website at www.nmm.ac.uk to discover how explorers in past times navigated their way around the globe using the sun and stars.

PE

- Use recorded music as a stimulus for dance work. A starting point could be 'going for a walk with your shadow' or working with a partner who mirrors their movements in the role of a shadow. 'Promenade – walking the Dog' from *Shall we dance* by George Gershwin or *The entertainer* by Scott Joplin could be suitable pieces for such work.

A sundial works by casting a shadow onto a fixed, flat surface, marked with the hours of the day.

PSHCE

- Introduce the scenario of walking home from school on a dark winter afternoon. Ask groups of children to talk about ways that they could keep safe. Each group should nominate a 'scribe' whose role it is to jot down ideas on stick-it notes which can then be collected together and discussed as a class. Emphasise the importance of being visible to traffic and the ways in which this might be achieved.

- Invite a road-user in to talk to the children about pedestrians from a car driver's point of view, for instance, what is it like for a driver when a child runs out into the road in front of them in poor light?

Cut out these pictures of time pieces. The dates show when they were used. Then put them in chronological (time) order.

pendulum clock

1676

silver pocket watch

1850

digital watch

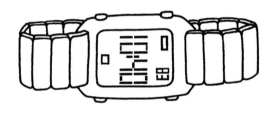

2008

sand glass

1348

candle clock

1012

sundial

1480

cut

cut

cut

Find out all you can about the history of sundials.

Geography

● Using a globe as a reference point, discuss the 24 hour time zones used on our planet. Talk about the Earth's 24 hour journey about its own axis and its annual 365 day trip around the sun (see the display above).

● Visit the Royal Observatory at Greenwich or the National Maritime Museum website at www.nmm.ac.uk to find out information about the prime meridian at Greenwich and why it is that Greenwich was chosen as having Longitude 0 degrees; also why locations around the world are measured according to their distance east or west from Greenwich in east London.

● List countries that children have visited which are 'behind' our time, such as the United States, and the countries that are 'ahead' such as India, Thailand and Australia. Find these places on a globe or on a large map of the world.

Art

● Provide the children with a limited colour palette of paints, such as restricting them to the use of dark blues, purple and black, to create a painted image representative of darkness and shadow.

● Go into the playground on a bright sunny day and ask children to create temporary images on the playground surface, by drawing around their shadows using brightly coloured chalks.

● Use a strong light source such as an anglepoise lamp to shine on objects and ask the children to make observational still-life drawings of objects and their shadows.

● Look at paintings by J. M. W. Turner (1775–1851), such as *The lake, Petworth, sunset*, and discuss the effects created by the use of colour and light. The Tate Gallery website www.tate.org.uk may be a useful place to search for other images and resource materials.

RE

- Evaluate the role of light in a variety of religions. Find out about how light is used in celebrations and festivals.

- In the Bible Jesus describes himself as being "The light of the World". Talk about what this means to a Christian (see display above).

- Visit a local church or other religious building. Look at the stained glass windows from the outside and then from inside. Talk about the effects that the light coming through the glass into the building has on the images and on creating a special sense of place inside.

Design & Technology

- Evaluate a collection of high-visibility items such as reflective strips, badges, tabards or jackets. Use this as a starting point for generating design ideas for a high-visibility item for a child, such as an armband that could be worn on the sleeve on a coat.

- Ask the children to design and make a product such as an armband, then test out whether it meets the design intention, for instance by demonstrating that the armband will fit over the sleeve of a coat, and by wearing the armband in a dark place and shining a torch onto it to assess its reflective qualities.

Music

- Sing popular songs such as *Me and my shadow* and *On the sunny side of the street*. They have been sung by Frank Sinatra, Perry Como and Bing Crosby. These could be rehearsed and performed in an assembly or to another class.

- Using percussion and tuned instruments, ask groups of children to compose a piece of music that is an interpretation of an artwork, such as a landscape by J. M. W. Turner. Focus the children's thinking on how to use musical elements such as timbre and pitch to suggest the visual elements of light and shadow in the painting.

- Use a tape recorder to make a recording of the children's work. Play the recording as an accompaniment to a PowerPoint® slideshow of images by an artist such as Turner.

Magnets and Springs

These grids demonstrate the learning objectives covered in the activities within the theme. The curriculum references indicate the relevant programme of study (PoS) for a subject area unless otherwise stated.

	Learning Objectives	Curriculum References
Science (Page 66)		
Scientific Enquiry	Gather information about springs and magnets.	Sc1/2b; ICT PoS 1a
	Discuss ideas and hypotheses, make predictions.	Sc1/2c
	Plan and carry out an investigation involving magnets to find answers and solutions.	Sc1/1b
	Consider the need for fair testing.	Sc1/2d
Physical Processes (QCA Science Unit 3E)	Understand that magnets have north and south poles which attract and repel other magnets and magnetic objects.	Sc4/2a
	Observe magnets attracting magnetic materials.	Sc4/2a
	Use a push force to compress a spring.	Sc4/2d
	Use a Newton meter to measure a force.	Sc4/2e
Materials and their Properties	Identify magnetic and non-magnetic materials.	Sc3/1a
	Compare different types of magnet.	Sc3/1a
Literacy (Page 68)		
Speaking	Speak to an audience about what life would be like without magnets and springs.	En1/1c
Understanding and Interpreting Texts	Read non-fiction texts about magnets and springs to gather information.	En2/3a,c
	Read adverts and magazine articles featuring toys that use magnets and springs.	En2/9c
Creating and Shaping Texts	Plan and write a story for a known character.	En3/9a
	Use email as a means to share information about magnets and springs.	En3/1a;9b; ICT PoS 3a
	Create a rhyming poem from key words or topic information.	En3/1c
Mathematics (Page 70)		
Calculating	Use written methods to calculate the addition of three numbers.	Ma2/3i
Understanding Shape	Explain features of shape and space using spirals as a starting point.	Ma3/2b
	Draw spirals using a compass.	Ma3/2c
	Describe patterns using appropriate vocabulary.	Ma3/2c
Measuring	Use a Newton meter to make measurements.	Ma3/4b

Magnets and Springs

Learning Objectives	Curriculum References
Design & Technology (Page 72)	
Generate and develop design ideas for a magnetic toy and fridge magnet.	PoS 1a,b
Explore the use of moving mechanisms in items containing springs.	PoS 4c
Disassemble common objects containing springs.	PoS 5a
Use a variety of materials to create products.	PoS 5c
Music (Page 72)	
Listen to and appraise music suggestive of springs and bounces.	PoS 3a,b;4a
Choose and combine sounds to create a deliberate effect.	PoS 2b
Use a kangaroo as a starting point for composition.	PoS 5b
Geography (Page 74)	
Use a compass during fieldwork.	PoS 2b
Study the interdependence of people, goods and materials travelling around the globe using a compass.	PoS 3g
Recognise behavioural patterns that occur due to the Earth's magnetic field.	PoS 4a
History (Page 74)	
Find out about compass use in the past using a range of sources of information.	PoS 4a; ICT PoS 1a;5b
Explore changes in seafaring and navigation.	PoS 2c,d;11b
Research information on famous people from the past, such as Robert Hooke and Ernest Shackleton.	PoS 4a
Art (Page 75)	
Generate ideas from springs as a starting point for work.	PoS 1b
Observe the tactile and visual aspects of a range of media such as iron filings.	PoS 2a;4a
Create a spring sculpture.	PoS 5c
Experiment with and use folding techniques to create springy animals.	PoS 2b
PE (Page 75)	
Perform controlled springy and bouncy actions.	PoS 1b
Rehearse sequences of movements to create a 'magnet' dance.	PoS 6a

Magnets and Springs

Science

Starting points

- Talk about everyday uses for magnets and springs. For example, magnets can be found in toys and games, as closing mechanisms on cupboard doors, in compasses, in metal detectors and in tools such as screwdrivers. Springs can be found in toys such as trampolines, slinkys and pogo sticks, inside clocks, watches and kitchen scales and in garage door mechanisms.

- Explain the concept of like poles repelling each other and unlike poles attracting using roleplay. Ask two children to each be the south pole of a magnet and two more children to be the north pole of a magnet. When the two like poles meet, they will push away from each other, but when the two unlike poles meet they will come together for a hug!

- Provide an opportunity to handle a range of springs. Encourage the children to experience for themselves the push force needed to compress a spring, then carefully allowing the spring to reform to its starting shape. Safety glasses should be worn for this activity. Create a display to show this (see above).

Enquiry

- Demonstrate to the children a way of testing the strength of a magnet by observing how many paper clips a magnet will pick up from a table top when it is held just above the clips. Repeat with two or three different magnets. Now challenge the children, working in teams, to come up with their own way to test the strength of a selection of magnets. Ask them to think about what they already know about magnets and about the demonstration that you showed them. Ask them to consider how they will keep the test fair and how they will record and then present their findings. If the children need a little prompting, you could suggest trying out the strength of a magnetic field through different thicknesses of paper or card.

Extension

- Most children know that magnets attract metallic, but not non-metallic, objects. Pose the question *'Are ALL metals attracted to a magnet?'* Provide the children with a selection of everyday objects made from different metals and ask the children to predict then test the objects using a magnet (see the activity sheet on page 67). What can the children tell you as a result of their testing? What property do magnetic metals have in common?

METALS and MAGNETS

Are all metals magnetic? Test some different metals and find out!

PREDICT

Put a tick next to the metals you think WILL be magnetic.

☐ copper ☐ gold ☐ steel

☐ silver ☐ aluminium

☐ brass ☐ iron ☐ zinc

TEST

See if any of these metallic objects are attracted to a magnet.

A GOLD ring	**Some COPPER wire**	**A BRASS screw**	**Some ALUMINIUM foil**
Magnetic?	Magnetic?	Magnetic?	Magnetic?
☐ Yes ☐ No	☐ Yes ☐ No	☐ Yes ☐ No	☐ Yes ☐ No

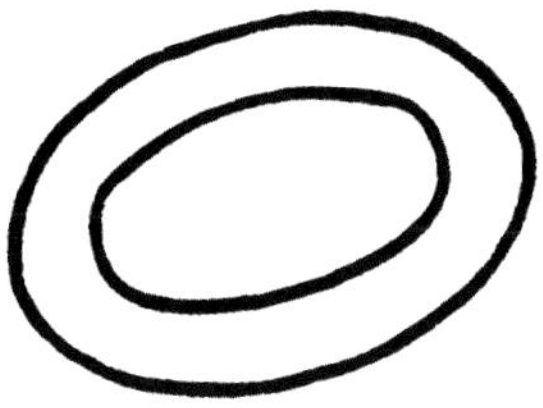

A STEEL can	**A SILVER necklace**	**A ZINC bucket**	**An IRON nail**
Magnetic?	Magnetic?	Magnetic?	Magnetic?
☐ Yes ☐ No	☐ Yes ☐ No	☐ Yes ☐ No	☐ Yes ☐ No

NOW!

Talk about your results.
Were they what you expected?
What can you conclude from your testing?

SPRING into a story with FIZZ KID LIZ by Linda Strachan.

Fizz Kid Liz has made her springy pogo stick into a time travelling machine! WOW!

Boing! She bounces back in time. Read this story to find out what happens...

Literacy

Speaking and Listening

● Challenge class members to talk for one whole minute, without pausing, about what life would be like without magnets and springs.

● Exchange and share information with others by email about things that use magnets and springs.

Reading and Writing

● Read non-fiction texts such as *Magnets* by Lesley Wing Jan (Rigby), *The mystery of magnets* by Melvin Berger (Newbridge) and *How does it work?* by David Glover (Dorling Kindersley).

● Read *Fizz Kid Liz* by Linda Strachan (Rigby). Liz pretends that her pogo stick is a time travelling device. Ask the children to plan and write their own new adventure for Liz (see the display above for some ideas).

● Look at the organisational features found in non-fiction texts and use as a basis for creating a class big book text about magnets and springs.

● Read advertisements from magazines or websites for toys with springs or magnets. Ask the children to write their own advert for a magnet toy, using the activity sheet on page 69.

● Write an acrostics poem, beginning with the word magnet or spring.

● Write an alliterative tongue-twister about a spring.

Fizz Kid Liz has made her springy pogo stick into a time travelling machine! WOW!

Boing! She bounces back in time. Read this story to find out what happens...

Magnets and Springs

Advertising works!

Design an advert for a new spring or magnet toy. Think about the persuasive language you will use. Can you add a memorable catchphrase?

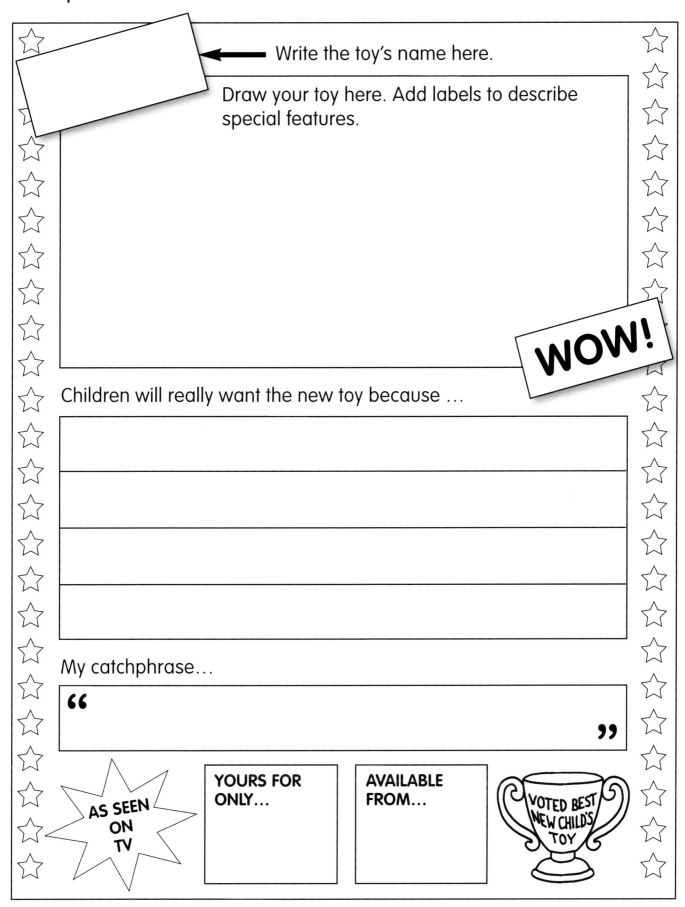

Write the toy's name here.

Draw your toy here. Add labels to describe special features.

WOW!

Children will really want the new toy because …

My catchphrase…

"   "

AS SEEN ON TV

YOURS FOR ONLY…

AVAILABLE FROM…

VOTED BEST NEW CHILD'S TOY

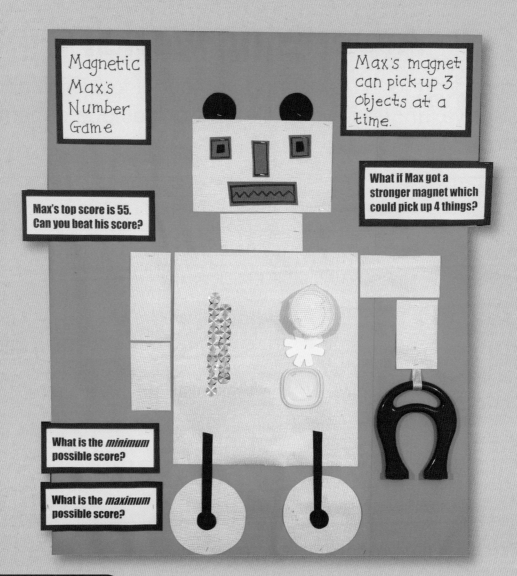

Magnetic Max's Number Game

Max's magnet can pick up 3 objects at a time.

Max's top score is 55. Can you beat his score?

What if Max got a stronger magnet which could pick up 4 things?

What is the *minimum* possible score?

What is the *maximum* possible score?

Maths

Calculating

● Play a 'magnetic fishing' type addition game such as that shown in the activity sheet (on page 71) or create a similar interactive wall display (see the display above). Here Max is using a magnet to collect items, the value of which must be calculated by addition.

Understanding Shape

● Look at the shape and pattern of coiled and spiral springs.

● Ask the children to find out what shape can be seen when a coiled spring is pulled out at either end.

● Look at the pattern of a spiral spring such as found inside a clock. Ask the children to look at examples of a spiral pattern in the natural world, such as in an ammonite fossil, spider web, tendrils of a climbing plant and a nautilus shell. Challenge the children to explain why this pattern is a commonly found template in the natural world.

● Challenge the children to draw their own spiral using a compass. Could they use a similar technique to draw a giant chalk spiral on the playground? How could this be achieved?

Measuring

● Ask the children to use a Newton meter to measure the force, in newtons, of a selection of classroom objects. Ask the children to think of the best way to present their findings.

Magnets and Springs

METAL MAX'S MAGNET GAME

CAN YOU ADD THREE NUMBERS?

Metal Max has a magnet which can pick up three objects at a time. Calculate the points that can be scored. You could play this game with a friend.

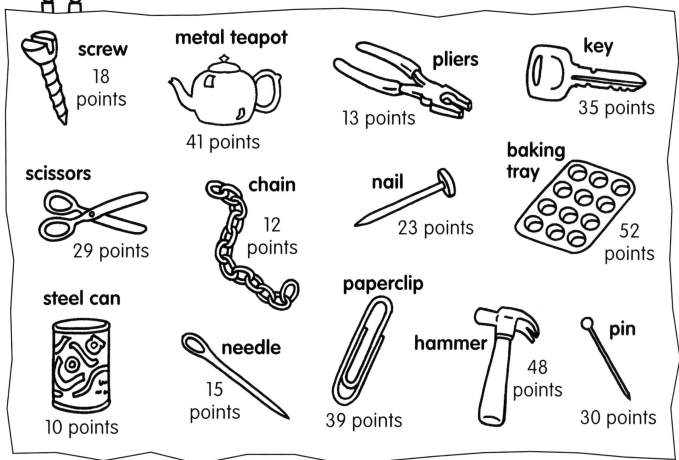

screw 18 points

metal teapot 41 points

pliers 13 points

key 35 points

scissors 29 points

chain 12 points

nail 23 points

baking tray 52 points

steel can 10 points

needle 15 points

paperclip 39 points

hammer 48 points

pin 30 points

Here's one that Max has done for you:

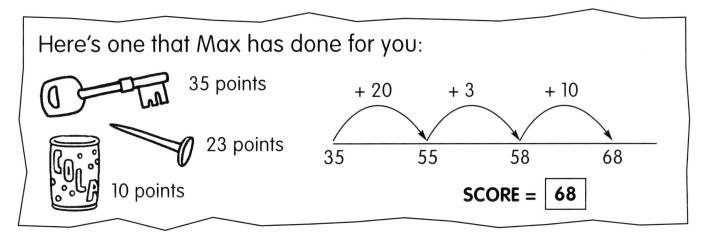

35 points

23 points

10 points

+ 20   + 3   + 10

35   55   58   68

SCORE = 68

NOW!

Work out the lowest possible score.
Then work out the highest possible score.

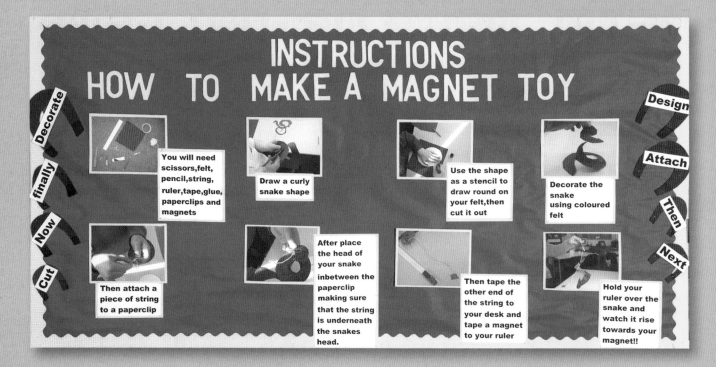

INSTRUCTIONS
HOW TO MAKE A MAGNET TOY

Decorate · finally · Now · Cut · Design · Attach · Then · Next

You will need scissors, felt, pencil, string, ruler, tape, glue, paperclips and magnets

Draw a curly snake shape

Use the shape as a stencil to draw round on your felt, then cut it out

Decorate the snake using coloured felt

Then attach a piece of string to a paperclip

After place the head of your snake inbetween the paperclip making sure that the string is underneath the snakes head.

Then tape the other end of the string to your desk and tape a magnet to your ruler

Hold your ruler over the snake and watch it rise towards your magnet!!

Design & Technology

● Take apart an item containing a spring, such as a retractable ballpoint pen, to see how it works (see the activity sheet on page 73).

● Collect other examples where a spring has been used in everyday objects, such as in a jack-in-the-box toy.

● Make a classroom collection of different types of magnetic toy, such as fishing games, train sets and construction kits. Evaluate the toys, bearing in mind the purpose for which the magnet has been used.

● Ask the children to design and make their own magnet toy for a younger child (see the display above).

● Ask the children to make their own metal spring by using the technique of carefully winding some malleable wire around a pencil. Wearing safety glasses, they should compress and release their spring.

● Ask the children to make a folded paper 'spring' and use as a pop-up mechanism inside a greetings card.

● Evaluate a collection of fridge magnets and then ask the children to design one of their own using thick card and adhesive magnetic strip.

Music

● Use the idea of 'springy' animals such as frogs, kangaroos, grasshoppers and fleas as a starting point for the composition of a piece of music. Begin by investigating ways to create sounds, which bring to mind springy, bouncy movements.

● Listen and respond to the 'Kangaroo' music from *The carnival of animals* by Camille Saint-Saëns (1835–1921) and discuss how musical elements have been used to communicate an effect, which evokes the movement of the animal.

● Play recordings of *Jack-in-a-box, pantomime for piano-prelude* by Erik Satie and *Jeux d'enfants: le volant* by Georges Bizet (1838–1875) and ask the children to visualise the movement of springs as they listen.

● Listen to a recording of *Pictures at an exhibition: the great gate of Kiev* by Modest Mussorgsky (1839–1881). Talk about how the effects of slow and stately piano music could be interpreted as giant springs gaining strength and bouncing up.

How does it work?

Taking a product apart can be a good way to evaluate how it works. Here is a retractable ballpoint pen:

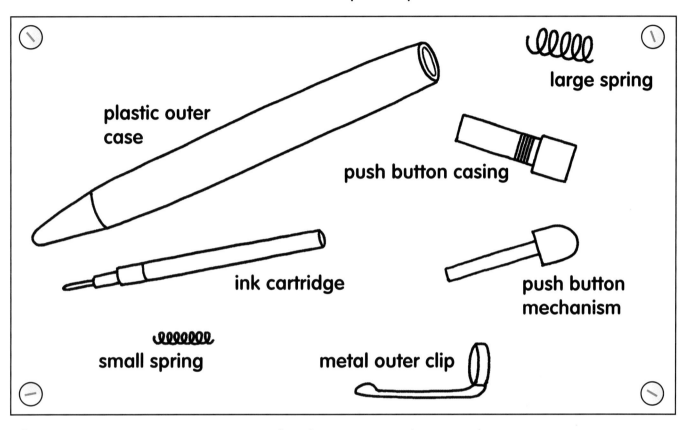

large spring

plastic outer case

push button casing

ink cartridge

push button mechanism

small spring

metal outer clip

There are two springs inside the pen. What is their purpose? Write your ideas here:

_____

_____

_____

_____

_____

 **NOW!**   Take a torch apart. Draw and label all of the parts.

Geography

- Use a globe or atlas to locate areas in the world where magnetite, a naturally occurring magnetic rock, can be found.

- Discuss how the magnetic compass enabled the world to be navigated.

- Practise using a compass to navigate a course around the playground or park.

- The manufacture of steel springs is an example of a current British manufacturing industry. Find out about the impact of this activity, in physical and human terms, in a localised area.

- The Earth acts just like a great big bar magnet, and produces a magnetic field, from the north and south poles, in the same way. The NASA website, www.science.nasa.gov, gives a brief explanation of this. Consider the physical effects that this has on migrating birds (see also the display).

History

- Use a range of sources including the internet to find out facts about the scientist Robert Hooke (1635–1703), who famously wrote the law of elasticity.

- Investigate the invention and subsequent use of a magnetic compass.

- Find out about early seafarers and explorers who used the compass to navigate the globe.

- Visit the National Maritime Museum website at www.nmm.ac.uk to gather information about navigation.

- Undertake a research project on the famous Edwardian explorer and hero Sir Ernest Shackleton (1874–1922) who led many expeditions in the Antarctic region and attempted to reach the South Pole. Visit websites such as www.bbc.co.uk/history/historic_figures or www.south-pole.com as a starting point for information gathering.

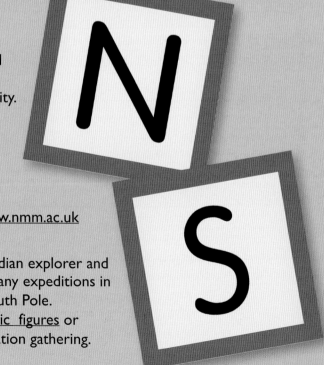

Art

- Create a temporary sculpture from an assortment of springs.

- Experiment with the technique of creating paper 'springs' by folding two strips of paper over each other to form a 'spring'. Try out different colours, thicknesses and widths of paper to create different effects.

- Use the paper 'springs' as the basis for a 'springy animal' model (see the display above). Use the springs for the arms, legs, body and feelers.

- Use spiral patterns in nature as a stimulus for creating spiral patterned artwork.

- Use the patterns created by iron filings in a magnetic field generated by a bar magnet as a starting point for an imaginative drawn image.

PE

- Create a springy dance using springy, bouncy animals as a starting point for movement sequences. Rehearse and perform the dance in small groups.

- Use a music stimuli such as the 'Kangaroo' from *The carnival of animals* by Camille Saint-Saëns (see also page 72 above).

- Listen to a recording of *Peer Gynt suite: Arabian dance* by Edvard Grieg (1843–1907). Ask the children to rehearse and perform a dance to this music that is suggestive of magnets repelling and being attracted to each other.

Assessment Ideas

In any activity the children carry out, whether through discussing, planning, doing or writing, there is an element of assessment. There are many ways to assess children – see the ideas below and the grid on page 77 for further suggestions. Knowledge-based assessments should use a variety of methods such as games, quizzes, drama and role play presentations, discussion of 'concept cartoons' and completing 'concept maps'.

● Concept cartoons are a useful tool in teaching and assessing. Each cartoon takes an everyday scientific idea about which three or more points of view are shown. For example, it could be a variety of views about how quickly objects fall. The cartoons encourage children to think carefully about what is being discussed and say which point of view they agree with and why. The cartoons generally portray a range of ideas which can be used to promote discussion of the children's own ideas and inform teachers what to teach and how to group children. For more information visit www.conceptcartoons.com

● Concept maps are also useful. The idea is to link nouns about a theme with arrows. The arrow shows the connection between the two words. For example:

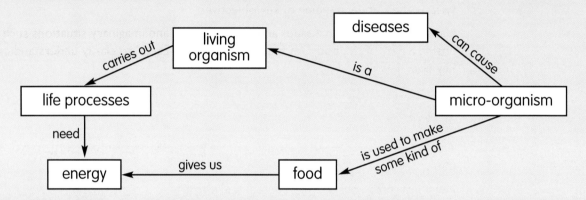

● Ensure that you have clear learning objectives for your lessons and that these are shared and understood by the children.

● Tell the children what the success criteria are and how they can achieve them.

● When marking children's work, highlight successes against the learning objective and write affirmative statements on the page, such as 'you can make a circuit' or 'you can name parts of the body'.

● Include time for assessment work in your daily and weekly planning. You may wish to conduct an end of topic investigation to access the children's level of knowledge and understanding.

● At the end of the topic, create a spreadsheet document to record the children's attainment against the objectives. Colour-code the cells: red for not achieved, orange for objective met and green for those who have exceeded expectations. This will produce an 'at a glance' reference to achievement and will highlight areas that need further work. Such documents could be handed on with other record-keeping to inform planning in subsequent year groups.

● Self-assessment sheets for children to complete are included on pages 78–80. The sheets cover areas of knowledge taught throughout the year. Children should be given their own sheets at the end of teaching a theme for them to colour in the objectives achieved. These could be colour-coded for those areas they think they know well/are uncertain about/do not know. The 'I can …' statements of skills will be practised in different contexts throughout the year, so children need to make judgements on each one more than once, again at the end of each theme and they should write the date in the column when the skill is achieved. Use all the sheets alongside your assessments to inform reports and general assessment at the end of the school year.

Who Should Assess?

Anyone involved with children's learning can assess, including parents and the children themselves. The most important thing is that the assessor knows what they are looking for and has the skills and knowledge to make these judgements. Children can assess each other – but they should always try to be constructive – what are the good points as well as the not so good?

HOW	TIPS
Observation of Children Working	Use this method when there is no written work as evidence, for example when children are planning and discussing.
	Assess a single child or a group by questioning the children to clarify understanding.
Group Feedback	Use this method to clarify the understanding of 'quiet' children, or those you are unsure about.
	Allow the 'listening' children to ask questions of 'presenters'.
	Ask questions of the children to gain a greater understanding of their learning.
Recording Children's Views During an Activity	Gather the children's opinions and ideas during activities.
	Ask the children to make their own recordings for you to listen to after the lesson.
Drama	This method is fun and non-threatening for children as they can 'show' instead of writing their understanding of key objectives.
	Use role play to discuss issues and act out events and imaginary situations such as, 'inside a part of the body', 'in space' or 'inside the Earth' to clarify understanding of key concepts.
Concept Cartoons	Use at the beginning and/or at the end of lessons to clarify children's ideas.
Diagrams, Drawings and Photographs	Ask the children to draw ideas before teaching and at the end to compare understanding of concepts.
	Make/interpret concept maps before and after lessons/topics.
	Photograph the children's work before/after the topic is complete to compare.
Sort a Collection	Ask the children to sort a collection of objects/vocabulary related to the topic in different ways.
	This method is particularly good for maths and science, to pinpoint the children's grasp of skills and knowledge.
Make & Play a Game	Incorporate key concepts and vocabulary into games, for example create questions that the children have to answer correctly before they move a space on a board game.
	Laminate games and retain for future use.
Devise & Answer Questions	Put questions in a box (generated by the teacher and the children) and ask the children to answer them over the course of the topic.
Interactive Display	Put questions on displays which highlight key concepts instead of labels.
	Add to the display as the topic progresses.
Types of Quiz	Create a true/false quiz on areas of knowledge and play this before and after teaching the topic to compare the children's responses.
	Quizzes can be oral or written by the children or teacher.
Written Work	Writing is useful as evidence but be aware that this is not always the best way for children to demonstrate what they know or can do.
	Use different genres of writing.

Life Processes and Living Things

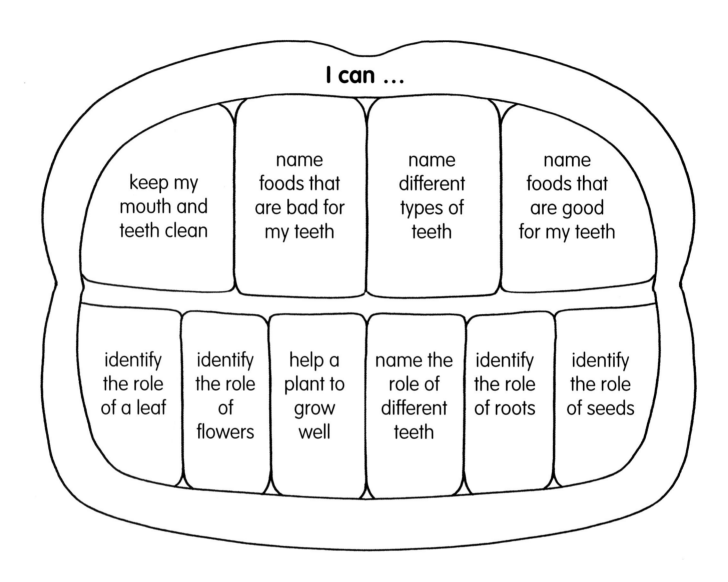

I can …

- keep my mouth and teeth clean
- name foods that are bad for my teeth
- name different types of teeth
- name foods that are good for my teeth
- identify the role of a leaf
- identify the role of flowers
- help a plant to grow well
- name the role of different teeth
- identify the role of roots
- identify the role of seeds

Scientific Enquiry

I can …

Skill	Date	Date	Date	Skill	Date	Date	Date
ask questions about things around me				talk about the things I need to do to keep a test fair			
suggest ways of answering questions				understand the need for a control sample			
share ideas with others and choose the best idea				make and record observations			
make a prediction				compare my prediction to the actual result			
validate my prediction with an explanation				describe what has happened and why to others			

Materials and their Properties

I can …

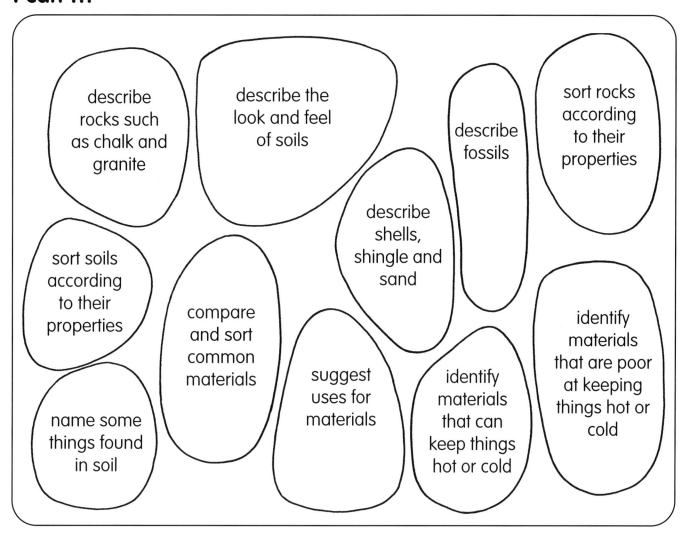

- describe rocks such as chalk and granite
- describe the look and feel of soils
- describe fossils
- sort rocks according to their properties
- sort soils according to their properties
- describe shells, shingle and sand
- compare and sort common materials
- identify materials that are poor at keeping things hot or cold
- name some things found in soil
- suggest uses for materials
- identify materials that can keep things hot or cold

Scientific Enquiry

I can …

Skill	Date	Date	Date	Skill	Date	Date	Date
ask questions about things around me				talk about the things I need to do to keep a test fair			
suggest ways of answering questions				understand the need for a control sample			
share ideas with others and choose the best idea				make and record observations			
make and explain a prediction				Review what has happened and explain it to others			
Take account of risks to stay safe				Compare my prediction to the actual result			

Physical Processes

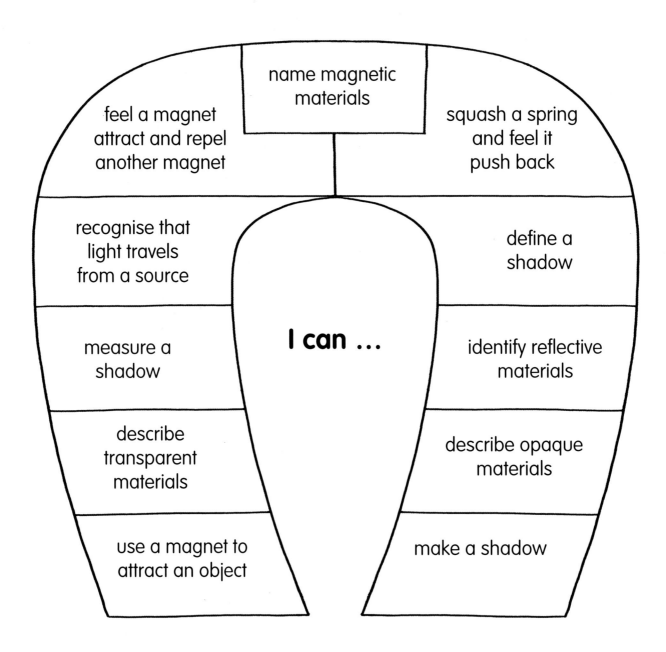

name magnetic materials

feel a magnet attract and repel another magnet

squash a spring and feel it push back

recognise that light travels from a source

define a shadow

I can ...

measure a shadow

identify reflective materials

describe transparent materials

describe opaque materials

use a magnet to attract an object

make a shadow

Scientific Enquiry

I can ...

Skill	Date	Date	Date	Skill	Date	Date	Date
ask questions about things around me				make and record observations and measurements			
suggest ways of answering questions				use equipment appropriately			
decide and plan what to do				compare my prediction to the actual result			
talk about the things I need to do to keep a test fair				review what has happened and explain it to others			
make and explain a prediction				use appropriate scientific language in my explanations			